Sugar-Free Cakes and Biscuits

SUGAR-FREE CAKES AND BISCUITS

Recipes for diabetics and dieters

Elbie Lebrecht

faber and faber

LONDON · BOSTON

First published in 1985
by Faber and Faber Limited
3 Queen Square London WC1N 3AU
Filmset by Wilmaset Birkenhead Wirral

Printed in Great Britain by
Whitstable Litho Ltd Whitstable Kent

British Library Cataloguing in Publication Data

Lebrecht, Elbie
Sugar-free cakes and biscuits.
1. Diabetes — Diet therapy — Recipes
I. Title
641.5'6314   RC662
ISBN 0-571-13668-0

CONTENTS

ACKNOWLEDGEMENTS

Jasmine Challis, dietitian at St Bartholomew's Hospital, London, gave me invaluable help in checking the carbohydrate and calorie counts and compiling the food table. I am indebted both for her expert advice and her open-mindedness. Pat Cox provided valuable advice on freezing and Jill Metcalfe, dietitian at the British Diabetic Association, gave me encouragement at an early stage when it was most needed. My grateful thanks to them all.

For recipe ideas and suggestions I am indebted in particular to Rachel Simon, and also to Caro Bailey, Miriam Erntroy, Sheila Ford, Irene Frohlich, Muriel Goldberg, Esther Levy, Beatrice Maltz and Erna Weiss. None of this would have been possible without the dedicated work of Dr Flynn and the staff of the Children's Ward and Clinic at the Royal Free Hospital, London.

My husband has been a continual source of encouragement and support and he and my girls, Naama and Abigail, have been very good-natured about being used as guinea pigs. Without them this book would never have been written.

INTRODUCTION

The recipes in this book were begun in response to my three-year-old daughter becoming diabetic. Once we had got over the initial shock and despair, we slowly learned to cope with a regime of daily injections, measuring out amounts of food, organizing meals at fixed hours and remembering to leave the house with provisions for a possible hypo (low blood sugar) crisis. There was a lot for us to come to grips with, and it took many months before the restrictions became routine. Against this background of having to give undue attention to food and its new rules, it seemed terribly important that we should feel we were leading as normal a life as possible. 'Normal' meant still having cakes and sweet treats to enjoy with a hot drink or to chat over with friends.

From the outset we decided as a family to eliminate sugar altogether. Until then, I suppose, we had conformed to the UK and US average for sugar consumption – around 90 lb per person per year, just under one kilo of sugar a week. We also had to cut out honey, since it has the same effect as sugar on the diabetic constitution.

Our decision to avoid artificial sweeteners was more tricky since professional reports of their effect and supposed harmlessness varied widely. Some studies showed saccharin to be linked to a cancer risk; sorbitol causes tummy upsets when taken in excess; recent research suggests that fructose is more readily absorbed by the body than has previously been assumed. Other sweeteners that have lately come on the market are chemically synthesized and far removed from any natural source. As non-scientists, the simplest conclusion seemed to be that we would be healthiest if we could get by without artificial sweeteners.

My husband, in his first anguished response to Naama's illness, threw out of the house every product containing sugar. We soon realized that this was not enough. A diabetic needs to eat especially nutritiously and sugar was not the only element in our diet. Refined foods such as white flour, white bread, white rice, spaghetti made from refined flour, had to be replaced by natural products. As time went on and we began to understand more about the food we eat, our style of eating and food buying changed considerably. It is ironic that diabetes should have led us all to a more positively healthy diet.

Through trial and error I worked out recipes for cakes and biscuits using dried and fresh fruit. I began to understand how these ingredients worked and the results started to taste very good, not just to us, but to a wide range of visiting friends. We discovered that it was possible to eat healthily and sweetly at the same time. We also discovered that over a long period of time we had lost excess weight by adhering to a sugar-free, low-fat and high-fibre diet.

WHY NO SUGAR?

Our decision to live without sugar was an emotional response to the advent of diabetes. Only much later did I begin to examine the available scientific and popular literature. As a lay person I had to find my way through a labyrinth of conflicting ideas, discover which were consensus opinions and which were contentious.

For me, the case against sugar was put most clearly by Surgeon-Captain T. L. Cleave, who worked in different parts of the world for many years before publishing his conclusions on refined sugar in 1956. He observed that refined sugar – the white or brown sugar that we buy in the shops – had 90 per cent of the original sugar-cane or sugar-beet removed from it. With almost all of the plant having been discarded, this means that one generous teaspoon of refined sugar contains the same amount of natural sugar as a whole apple. Consider how quickly you can swallow a generous teaspoon of sugar and how long it takes to eat an apple, or to drink a cup of sweet tea with three sugars and to consume three apples – which are anyway more than the average person can eat at a single session. Cleave concludes that eating sugar sends the stomach a false message. It does not feel full in the way that it would from, say, apples and continues to demand more food. Consequently eating refined sugar leads to an over-consumption of food to fill the stomach. Cleave blames this form of overeating on the concentrated sugar; the body is equipped to cope with natural foods in normal quantities. As a result of too much food, the body's system becomes overloaded and may develop serious conditions such as obesity and its disorders.

'YOU MUST HAVE SUGAR IN YOUR DIET'

Well-intentioned relatives, hearing of our attempt at sugar-free eating warned solemnly: 'You need sugar – especially when you are short of energy.' Their concern proved unfounded; our energy needs are derived more beneficially from natural foods. Sugar contains scarcely any nutrients of value; it contains no vitamins and no fibre.

Refined sugar gives a raw burst of energy, then a drop into tiredness. Because the sugar is so processed it is not digested slowly by the body but rushes into the bloodstream, raising the blood sugar level. More insulin is produced in the pancreas (of non-diabetics) to take the sugar out of the blood, but the subsequent drop in blood sugar makes you feel tired and low; you need more sugar to pick you up.

The body creates the sugar for its energy needs during the process of digesting carbohydrates. Unrefined carbohydrates – such as whole grains, beans and vegetables – are digested and released into the bloodstream more slowly because of their fibre content, avoiding the sudden onslaught effect of refined sugars.

Our relatives were right – the body does need sugars, not the refined kind, but those that are broken down naturally from unrefined carbohydrates.

DRIED FRUITS – SO SWEET

Dried fruits not only make food sweet but are a health-giving food in their own right. They contain minerals, vitamins and fibre and have a low calorie count. The fibre content is proportionally higher in dried fruits than in fresh fruits because once the moisture is removed the fibre-rich skin predominates. Apricots are particularly rich in fibre with 24 grams per 100 grams of fruit, figs have 18.5 grams per 100 grams and prunes 16.1 grams per 100 grams. Dates are not so high in fibre but still contain four times as much as fresh apples, pears or oranges.

Sugar, compared to dried fruit (see table), has nothing to offer you in the way of minerals. Even if you allow for the fact that your body will not necessarily obtain all the minerals available in the dried fruit, they can only improve your supply of minerals.

Mineral content of sugar and dried fruits

	Sodium mg	Potassium mg	Calcium mg	Magnesium mg	Phosphorus mg	Iron mg	Copper mg	Zinc mg
Sugar	–	2	2	–	–	–	0.02	–
Apricots	56	1880	92	65	120	4.1	0.27	0.2
Dates	5	750	68	59	64	1.6	0.21	0.3
Figs	87	1010	280	92	92	4.2	0.24	0.9
Prunes	12	860	38	27	83	2.9	0.16	–
Raisins	52	860	61	42	33	1.6	0.24	0.1
Sultanas	53	860	52	35	95	1.8	0.35	(0.1)

(McCance and Widdowson, *The Composition of Foods*, 1979) (Measurements are per 100 grams of dried fruit)

Apricots and prunes are particularly good sources of vitamin A and all dried fruits contain some of the B vitamins.

Dried fruits contain about half the calories of sugar and fructose, which have 100 calories per 25 grams (1 oz). Dates, sultanas, raisins and figs have 60, while 25 grams of apricots and prunes have around 40 calories.

Insulin-dependent diabetics, who have to keep to a carbohydrate count, know that dried fruit is not free of carbohydrates. I have tried to compensate for this in recipes by balancing them with other ingredients that have a low carbohydrate value.

WHY NOT FORGET ABOUT CAKES?

If natural sugar is best for us, you may ask, why make cakes? Why not just eat fruits, vegetables, nuts and seeds? But cakes made with high fibre and healthy foods, and given their proper place in a well-balanced diet, can be both enjoyable and nutritious. Certainly experts agree that eating food in as natural a state as possible is healthiest. None the less we live in a world where food processing is a vast industry, which succeeds by means of attractive packaging and seductive advertising in making its products socially indispensable.

The pressures are at their most intense in the lives of children. I suddenly discovered that almost every children's book has a tea or birthday party with tables laden with cakes and biscuits. My daughter would gaze enraptured at the brightly coloured drawings of all these goodies, pretending to eat them from the pages. Children's television is littered with conscious and subliminal advertisments for sweets, chocolate and snacks. Winners of games at friends' birthday parties are rewarded with sweets. Rather than deprive Naama and ourselves of these sociable creature comforts, I tried to make many of them myself with healthy ingredients. She would have to accept that other people did eat cakes and ices with sugar in, but she would at least have an acceptable substitute. She still longs for the forbidden foods of other children, but I knew that success was at hand when she became really excited about my stuffed marzipan dates (p. 105), a grown-up treat that she could share.

A further difficulty arose with my husband, who comes from a long line of cake and sweet-eaters. He found he was suffering cravings, and would have to dash out to buy himself a bar of chocolate or an ice-lolly for rapid consumption. His needs, too, were gradually – though not yet totally – assuaged by naturally sweetened cakes and biscuits.

In order to wean ourselves away from forbidden foods I was forced to compete on the same terms. I learned that carrot cake made without sugar and with wholewheat flour is a good step on the path away from cakes composed mainly of sugar, high fat content and white flour. Because you have to chew your way through the fibre from the dried fruit and flour there are only so many slices you can eat at one session, however delicious the cake. Yet both taste buds and appetite are satisfied by little.

From starting to think about cakes I went on to apply similar principles to our whole diet. I gradually introduced more grains and additional legumes into the mainstay of our meals; but changes had to be unobtrusive. Over-enthusiasm on my part could lead to a solid wall of resistance from my family.

After about a year of eating cakes without sugar, strange things began to happen to our taste buds. I suddenly noticed that cooked onions were truly sweet – I was able to taste the sweetness in a vegetable as sugar was no longer dulling my senses. My husband, drinking unsugared lemon tea, claimed to taste sweetness in the lemon. When in Vienna, dropping in at one of the finest patisseries along the Kärntnerstrasse he no longer got the same pleasure from a Sacher Torte. Objectively he knew that it was meant to taste good but it no longer provided the same sensual excitement: his tongue kept isolating the high sugar and margarine content. We also found that cakes or biscuits made with synthetic sweetener left us feeling unusually thirsty.

WHY HIGH FIBRE?

The high-fibre argument was stated by Thomas Cogan more than 400 years ago in 1584: 'Browne bread . . . having much branne . . . fylleth the belly with excrements, and shortly descendeth from the stomacke.' Today it is more urgently expressed by nutritionists concerned with the health of the general population. The term 'high fibre' is commonly used to mean 100 per cent flours – flours that are ground from the whole grain – or grain that has not had the outer husk removed, such as brown rice. White flour or refined flour has had 30 per cent of the grain extracted, including the nutritious germ and most of the fibrous bran. Surgeon-Captain Cleave, while working as a naval doctor on a ship in the Second World War, found that bran in their diet prevented constipation among sailors. From wider global observations he noted that people who enjoyed unrefined diets were virtually free of major twentieth-century Western diseases such as diabetes, peptic ulcers, coronary thrombosis, haemorrhoids, diverticular disease and dental caries.

Wholewheat flour contains all the goodness and vitamins of the original grain. It does not lead to over-consumption because the bran absorbs water and bulks up in its passage through the body. The blood glucose level remains steadier when 100 per cent wholewheat flour is eaten because it is absorbed more slowly through the body than refined flour.

High fibre also means eating pulses and beans, potatoes in their skins and unpeeled apples and carrots. Nutritionists insist that all parts of grain, fruit and vegetables have a role to play in the human digestion. The advantage of high fibre food for diabetics and dieters is that it can give a fuller feeling than refined food and inhibit over-consumption.

Once I recognized the advantages of high fibre I decided to use all the different grains available. A lot of people complain about the heaviness of 100 per cent wholewheat flour. Try using brown rice flakes for a change and a lighter texture, or oats, that old Scottish staple, which are moist and taste nutty enough to be used in the marzipan recipe. Other grains used in the recipes are cornmeal, millet flakes, rye flour and brown rice flour. One advantage of living in a wealthy part of the world is that a great variety of grains are readily available.

LOW FAT

The recipes in this book follow the recommendations of the National Advisory Committee on Nutrition Education (NACNE) that people should reduce their fat intake to combat obesity-related conditions such as heart disease and diabetes. Some of the recipes contain no fat at all, the others use only polyunsaturated fats and, where milk is needed, skimmed milk has been used. The main point about fats is that whatever kind you use, the amount should be kept fairly low.

THE DIETER AND SUGAR-FREE CAKES

Slimming diets that result in rapid weight loss can be more dangerous than the obesity they are intended to reverse. Equally, diets that are based on intensive over-consumption of certain foodstuffs and total elimination of others can upset the delicate balance of bodily well-being and give rise to depression, feelings of deprivation and general lassitude. As soon as the regime is over, body and soul veer back towards their previous state. Weight loss as a result of a gradual change in eating habits is likely to be longer lasting. Eating sugar-free, low-fat, high fibre food helps you to lose weight gradually, without losing your resolve or your friends. All the recipes in this book are based on these three principles. In a relatively short time, your taste buds undergo a process of re-education: sugar or synthetic sweetener becomes too sweet and natural sweetness is preferred as a way of life. Staying at the right weight can mean for many people a new approach to eating that continues throughout their life. Eaten in moderation sugar-free cakes and biscuits provide that extra spice – delicious wholefood treats which do not make a diet seem too sombre or unrelenting.

LET THEM EAT CAKE – HEALTHILY

What these recipes mean is that you can enjoy the sweet treats of life without sugar and its artificial substitutes. Sugar-free does not mean that your imagination has to seize up. It is a challenge to spur you on to compete with all those exotic concoctions gracing the shelves of the bakers, grocers and supermarkets.

But cakes and biscuits – however wholesomely made – are peripheral foods, to be consumed within a balanced diet.

Healthy eating means taking all foods in moderation, even such health-packed ingredients as dried fruits. I tend to bake cakes only for the weekend, during the week serving the plainer teacakes and scones, which are essentially cereal, egg and milk. Cakes are a very concentrated form of food; a plate of pasta or rice, with the same carbohydrate value as a slice of cake, will be much more filling.

Cakes can be used, though, as a way of introducing your family to nutritious novelties. Our first experiences of pumpkin and aduki beans were in cakes; once we had acquired the taste, I was able to bring them into other dishes. So use cakes intelligently – as a snack, a treat, a celebration, a social grace, and a means of discovering exciting new foods.

HINTS ON USING THE RECIPES

HOW TO BUY AND
USE DRIED FRUITS

The dried fruits used in these recipes are sultanas, seedless raisins, dates, figs, apricots and prunes, all of which can be obtained fairly easily from a local grocer or supermarket. When buying dried fruit look for even-sized, even-coloured, plump, unblemished fruit.

Dates can be bought in blocks, where pitted dates and pieces have been pressed together, weighing about 250g (9 oz). They are much cheaper when sold like this but you will have to keep an eye open for the occasional stone. Whole *apricots* tend to be moister than apricot pieces which are usually quite hard and dry. If you do use the drier pieces, soak them in a little water for about four hours before use. *Figs* are sometimes sold in blocks, but are usually bought loose. *Prunes* come in different sizes. The larger they are, the less stones there are per 100 grams.

PREPARATION
Before using dried fruit always rinse it with cold running water through a colander or sieve to make sure it is clean. Some recipes require the fruit to be soaked. In these cases, don't throw away the water since it will have absorbed nutrients. Instead boil it up with the dried fruit until it evaporates.

Date paste: this is one of the basic sweeteners used in these recipes. Heat the chopped dates with a little water in a pan over a low heat until all the water is absorbed. If you use the date blocks it will become a thick mushy paste, but with chopped whole dates you will probably have to blend the date mixture to make it smooth.

Fig paste: as with date paste the chopped figs are cooked with a little water until it is absorbed and then blended. If you use fig blocks there is no need to blend.

ADDITIVES
Some dried fruits are treated with food-grade mineral oil or

sulphur to preserve fruit colour and to prevent bacterial growth. Limits on the use of sulphur are recommended by government health authorities of importing countries. Some experts believe that mild sulphuring presents no problems since much of the sulphur, they say, evaporates and washes off, but others urge buyers to seek dried fruit that has not been treated with any substance. Many wholefood shops stock dried fruit without additives. Make a point of reading contents labels and checking additives when buying dried fruit.

FREEZING

Freezing is always useful when you use a lot of homemade foods in your diet. A stock of food in the freezer relieves the pressure of suddenly catering for unexpected guests and is a welcome source of food if you find yourself ill in bed and unable to cook. The recipes in this book give quite modest quantities because of the shorter storage life of sugar-free cakes. You may want to double them for freezing purposes.

FREEZING METHOD

Once defrosted most sugar-free cakes only taste really fresh for 1–2 days and fruit pastry rolls for up to 2 days, so avoid freezing too large a piece. Subdivide the cake, wrapping each section separately in cling film or foil, label the sections with the name of the cake, date of freezing and amount of carbohydrates and calories, then pack them in a freezer bag or inside a suitable plastic container. Always eliminate as much air as possible from the packaging. When freezing cakes, remember that many spices become less strong after freezing. Avoid freezing decorated cakes as they will not look fresh when thawed; rather decorate them after thawing.

Biscuits can be frozen loose before packaging and then packed in suitable quantities in film or foil before putting in a freezer bag or plastic container.

THAWING CAKES AND BISCUITS

Cakes: avoid removing freezer wrappings before thawing otherwise moisture will be lost through the surface into the atmosphere and a drier cake will result.

Biscuits: be selective in the thawing methods you use for

biscuits. Thin crisp biscuits such as jam hearts may become soft when left in their wrappings during thawing, while thicker biscuits such as cardamom biscuits may benefit from becoming soft and moist.

Thawing in the oven: this is a good method for cakes such as pastry cheese cake and scones. They can be thawed in the oven for a warm fresh result and immediate serving. Wrap them in foil before freezing so they can easily be placed in a hot oven. If any cake is left over you will find that it is much drier than if the usual slower methods of thawing had been used.

STORAGE LIFE

Freezing is recommended for convenience rather than long-term storage. If you have a party or holiday coming up, the freezer is a useful tool to help you be prepared and free you from cooking.

MAXIMUM RECOMMENDED STORAGE LIFE

Cakes	3 months
Teacakes	3 months
Scones and muffins	3 months
Raw pastry	1 month
Biscuits	3 months
Fruit rolls	3 months
Petits fours and sweets	2 months

MEASUREMENTS

Measurements are given throughout in both metric (grams) and imperial (ounces) weights, but I would advise you to use metric throughout because it is difficult to give exact conversions and grams are more specific for small quantities. The difference between 25 and 30 grams, for example, is too small to be marked on imperial cooking measures.

HOW TO MAKE ONE SLICE EQUAL 10g CHO

The term '10g CHO' is a basic unit used in measuring diabetic food portions. Recipes have a habit of blithely saying 'makes 30 slices' while the reader is left with knife poised, wondering how to produce that number out of the home-baked marvel in front of him or her. Here are a few tips to make it easier.

Recipes that specify 16 slices can be baked in a 20 cm (8 inch) square tin. This can be cut with ease into 16 squares. Mark off 3 lines lengthways and 3 lines crossways to give squares of 5 cm (2 inches).

Some baking-equipment shops sell tins that have slices marked off on the base of the tin, so that the finished cake has indentations for slice divisions. If a tin is divided into 12 slices then it can be used for a cake that specifies 12 or 24 slices. These tins are worth shopping around for.

Paper cases are a handy way of ensuring that each cake is 10g CHO. This is particularly useful with children. If a cake specifies 18 slices and you are worried about cutting this exactly from a cake then just count out 18 paper cases on a tray and fill them equally.

Biscuits or scones: these give you a lot of leeway because dough can be manipulated more easily than raw cake mixture. Once you have made a recipe a couple of times it will be easy to gauge how thick or thin to roll the pastry to reach the specified number.

Pastry rolls: mark these off before you bake them. If the recipe specifies 12 slices, first mark a half-way line on the pastry roll, then mark these in half again. You now have four divisions and within each one mark off 2 lines to make the total of 12 slices. If you use the end of a sharp knife the divisions stay clear after baking and make serving very easy.

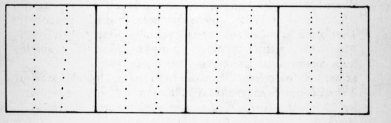

GLOSSARY OF INGREDIENTS

AGAR-AGAR is made from seaweed and used as a gelling agent. It comes in small flakes. Available from health food shops.

BARLEY FLOUR – ground from the whole grain, is an off-white colour. Available from health food shops.

BRAN – taken from the outer layers of the wheat grain, is a source of additional fibre. Available from health food shops, chemists and grocers.

BROWN RICE – rice which has not had the outer husk removed. Available from large supermarkets and health food shops.

BROWN RICE FLAKES – used in biscuits or as part of a breakfast cereal. Available from health food shops.

CAROB POWDER is a sweet, dark-brown powder that is ground from the fruit of the carob tree, which grows around the Mediterranean area. Available from health food shops.

CORNMEAL – ground corn or maize, is yellow and of coarse texture. Available from health food shops.

DRIED FRUIT VARIETIES – *dried apricots*, not as sweet as some of the other dried fruits but having a very distinctive taste, are produced in Australia, California, South Africa, Turkey and Iran. *Dates* are very sweet and grow in the Middle East and North Africa. *Prunes* are made from dried plums. The best known ones are Californian. *Raisins* are small and seedless dried grapes. They come mainly from California, South Africa and Afghanistan. *Sultanas*, also made from dried grapes, are soft and sweet. They are named after Smyrna in Turkey where they were originally produced. They come from Turkey, Greece, Australia, America and South Africa. Always check the labels for possible additives. Available from supermarkets, grocers and health food shops.

KOMBU – a dark-coloured seaweed from Japan. The salad kombu is shredded and can be broken off in clumps. Needs to be soaked for 30 minutes before eating raw. Available from health food shops.

MARGARINE – made from oils rich in polyunsaturated fats. Available from all grocers and supermarkets.

MILLET FLAKES – made from millet grains. These are also a useful addition to muesli or can be made into a mild porridge. Available from health food shops.

OAT BRAN AND GERM – taken from the oat grain. Oat bran is high in soluble fibre. Available from health food shops.

OILS – rich in polyunsaturated fats – include sunflower, safflower, soya bean and sesame seed oil. Available from health food shops. (Some nutritionists recommend that the best oils are those labelled cold-pressed, arguing that other extraction methods involve elaborate chemical processes. The practical drawback is that cold-pressed oils are much more expensive. A compromise is to avoid those oils that have 'refined' on their labels.)

POPPY SEEDS – these very small seeds are a dark blue colour. They are used to decorate bread and in cake making. Available from the spice section of most grocers and supermarkets.

PORRIDGE OATS – rolled oats available from all grocers, supermarkets, health food shops.

PUMPKIN SEEDS – small green seeds that have the outer shell removed. Available from health food shops.

RYE FLOUR – ground from the whole grain, similar in colour to wheat flour, but heavier and moister. Available from health food shops.

SESAME SEEDS – these tiny seeds are a light brown colour and may be used to decorate pies and cakes and make biscuits and sweets. Available from health food shops.

SKIMMED MILK QUARK – low fat soft cheese, available from large supermarkets and some grocers.

SOYA FLOUR – a pale yellow flour which is high in protein and low in carbohydrate. It is sold as low-fat or full-fat flour. The low fat variety is more suitable for a diabetic diet.

SUGAR-FREE JAM – jam made from 100 per cent fruit. Available from health food shops.

SUNFLOWER SEEDS – very small off-white seeds that have the hard outer shell removed. Available from health food shops.

TAHINI – made from ground sesame seeds. Popular in Greece, Turkey and the Middle East. Available from ethnic food stores, supermarkets and health food shops.

TOFU – soya bean curd. It originates from China and Japan, is low in calories and high in protein. The type I use is fresh, firm tofu, available from health food shops.

WHEAT GERM – the highly nutritious germ of the wheat. Once opened, store the packet in the fridge to avoid it turning rancid. Available from health food shops and chemists.

WHOLEWHEAT FLOUR* – flour that contains every part of the whole wheat grain – the bran, aleurone, germ and endosperm – and used in these recipes as the standard baking flour. Available from supermarkets, grocers and health food shops.

WHOLEWHEAT PASTRY FLOUR* – this is wholewheat flour ground twice to make a fine flour. It is harder to get hold of and so has not been specified in these recipes. Available from specialist health food shops.

*These flours can be bought in organic form, meaning that the grains have not been sprayed with chemicals but grown with natural fertilizer. The organic types tend to be slightly more expensive and not all health food shops supply them.

CAKES

Cakes, cakes, cakes. Memories of birthday parties, celebrations and tea parties. Cakes are a part of our Western culture. Not to be able to partake of them is to be left out of important eating rituals. These recipes provide the means for diabetics to eat cakes and be healthy. But although the recipes are based on high-fibre principles and contain no detrimental sweeteners they must be part of an overall balanced diet.

These cakes stay fresh for up to 2 days and should be stored in a tin or silver foil. Their life span is somewhat shorter than conventional cakes because sugar acts as a preservative. The cheesecakes last for up to 3 days and should be stored in a fridge.

All the cakes freeze well, and should be wrapped in foil or cling film and then put in a plastic freezer bag (see p. 19). The poppy seed cake seems to taste even moister after freezing. It is not worth freezing the cakes with icing on. They will look fresher if the icing is made on the same day that the cake is being served.

These cakes use either no egg or very little. The reason for this is that diabetics are advised to keep their egg consumption down; dietitians' recommendations vary from two eggs a week to four. It makes sense for cakes which are that 'special something' not to encroach on your egg allowance. To get the most out of an egg in your cake, beat it extremely well with a mixer or hand whisk. Even without sugar it can become thick and creamy. After the beaten egg has been added, fold in the remaining ingredients by hand; do not use a mixer or the air incorporated in the egg will be beaten out.

One advantage of making cakes without sugar and little or no eggs is that they very rarely flop. There is no delicate balance between the weight of sugar, eggs and flour. Bicarbonate of soda or yeast is used as the raising agent. The only precaution to remember is to include no more liquid than specified in the recipes.

These cakes are also very quick to make, requiring only that ingredients are mixed together in one bowl.

Including peel: apple peel and carrot skin should be included in the recipes where possible as they are a source of fibre. If they have been sprayed with chemicals while growing, and it is not possible to wash them off you will have to weigh up whether it is better to lower your intake of chemicals or increase your fibre intake.

FRUIT CAKES

Banana Cake

This is a light cake and I find it excellent to use as a base for decorated birthday cakes or special festive cakes.

75 g (3 oz) dried dates
50 ml (2 fl oz) water
225 g (8 oz) bananas, peeled, mashed finely
1 egg, size 3, well beaten
75 g (3 oz) wholewheat flour

25 g (1 oz) bran
1 tsp bicarbonate of soda
50 g (2 oz) ground almonds
½ tsp vanilla*
150 ml (5 fl oz) natural low-fat yogurt

Put dates and water in a pan over a low heat until the water is absorbed. Blend to an even smooth paste. Leave to cool.

Mash the bananas finely and add the cooled date paste. Add the well-beaten egg. Fold in the flour, bran, bicarbonate of soda and ground almonds. Stir in the vanilla and yogurt.

Lightly grease and flour a 20 cm (8 inch) diameter tin. Pour in the mixture. Bake in a preheated oven (gas 4/350°F/180°C) for 45 minutes until the cake is browned on top and the sides come away from the tin.

Makes 16 slices. Each slice is 10 g CHO. 70 kcals.

---

*You can make your own vanilla by using a vanilla pod. Either infuse it for 30 minutes in liquid used in the cake or else leave the pod in your flour jar and let the flavour be absorbed gradually.

Pineapple Fruit Cake

The pineapple in this cake makes it moist and easy to ⌐
recipe is delicious for all times but I've found it especially use⌐
for tempting convalescents' appetites.

75 g (3 oz) dried figs, chopped
50 ml (2 fl oz) water
275 g (10 oz) fresh pineapple
(remove outer skin before
weighing; if out of season use
canned unsweetened
pineapple, drained)

25 g (1 oz) sultanas
1 egg, size 3, well beaten
25 g (1 oz) ground almonds
25 g (1 oz) pumpkin seeds,
ground
25 g (1 oz) wheat germ
75 g (3 oz) wholewheat flour

Put the figs and water in a pan over a low heat and cook until the
water is absorbed and the fruit has become mushy. If the fig
pieces remain very large then work the mixture in a blender.
Leave to cool.

Chop the pineapple into 1 cm ($\frac{1}{2}$ inch) square pieces and
mix with the sultanas and fig paste. Add the egg,
beaten to a creamy consistency. Fold in the ground almonds,
ground pumpkin seeds, wheat germ and flour.

Lightly grease and flour an 18 cm (7 inch) diameter tin. Pour in
the mixture. Bake in a preheated oven (gas 3–4/325–350°F/
170–180°C) for 35–40 minutes until browned on top and a knife
inserted in the centre comes out cleanly.

Makes 8 slices. Each slice is 20 g CHO. 130 kcals.

Rice Fruit Cake

The combination of succulent fruit with tahini and a suggestion of
coconut in this cake gives it an unusual but delicious taste. A
good recipe for anyone unable to eat wheat flour.

100 g (4 oz) brown rice flour
25 g (1 oz) unsweetened
desiccated coconut
25 g (1 oz) tahini
1 tsp grated lemon rind
50 g (2 oz) dried dates

50 ml (2 fl oz) water
1 egg, size 3
175 g (6 oz) fresh pineapple
(remove outer skin before
weighing)
100 g (4 oz) fresh dates

Mix rice flour, coconut, tahini and lemon rind. Put the dried dates and water in a small pan and cook over a low heat until a thick paste is formed. Take off heat and leave to cool, then add to the flour mixture.

Beat the egg and stir in. Cut the pineapple and fresh dates into small bite-size pieces, removing stones from the dates. Mix in carefully so that they are well coated with the mixture. As a large proportion of this cake is fruit, with the egg and flour holding it all together, be careful not to crush the fruit as you stir it in. It is not advisable to use a food processor or mixer at this stage because the fruit could be broken down into too small pieces.

Grease and flour an 18 cm (7 inch) diameter tin. Pour in the mixture and bake in a preheated oven (gas 4/350°F/180°C) for 45 minutes until it is browned on top and a knife inserted in the centre comes out cleanly.

Makes 8 small slices. Each slice is 20 g CHO. 125 kcals.

Peach-Apple-Carob Swirl

The peach gives this cake a lovely tangy flavour. It looks very attractive with each slice a mixture of brown and white. A pink coconut cream topping (see p. 114) makes a very pretty effect.

2 large eating apples, weighing 300 g (11 oz), peeled and chopped
100 ml (4 fl oz) water
50 g (2 oz) dried dates
100 g (4 oz) wholewheat flour
25 g (1 oz) low-fat soya flour
50 g (2 oz) brown rice flakes
1 tsp bicarbonate of soda
2 tsp cream of tartar
2 ripe peaches, weighing 300 g (11 oz), peeled and chopped into 1 cm ($\frac{1}{2}$ inch) pieces
10 g ($\frac{1}{2}$ oz) carob powder

Put the peeled and chopped apples in a liquidizer with 50 ml (2 fl oz) water, and purée. Then set aside until needed.

Heat the dates with 50 ml (2 fl oz) water in a small pan. Cook until the water is absorbed and a thick paste is formed.

In a large bowl mix together the wholewheat flour, soya flour, rice flakes, bicarbonate of soda and cream of tartar. Now add the date paste to the flours together with the chopped peach pieces and the apple purée. Put half the mixture in a separate bowl and fold in the carob powder.

Grease and flour a 20 cm (8 inch) diameter tin. Dot tablespoon-fuls of the carob mixture into the tin, then fill in the gaps with the uncoloured mixture, making sure the whole surface of the tin is covered. Bake in a preheated oven (gas 4/ 350°F/180°C) for 45–50 minutes until the cake is firm and browned on top.

Makes 20 small slices. Each slice is 10 g CHO. 45 kcals (without icing); 55 kcals (with coconut cream icing).

Apple Cake

50 g (2 oz) dried dates, chopped	1 tsp bicarbonate of soda
75–100 ml (3–4 fl oz) water	1 tsp cinnamon
3 eating apples, weighing 350 g	$\frac{1}{8}$ tsp ground cloves
(12 oz), peeled and chopped	25 g (1 oz) sultanas, soaked in
150 g (5 oz) wholewheat flour	water
25 g (1 oz) low-fat soya flour	1 egg, size 3, well beaten
25 g (1 oz) ground almonds	

Put the dates and 50 ml (2 fl oz) water in a small pan and cook over a low heat until the water is absorbed. Blend and leave to cool. Either purée the apples directly in a blender with 25–50 ml (1–2 fl oz) water or cook with a little water in a saucepan until softened, then beat to a purée.

Mix the flours, ground almonds, bicarbonate of soda and spices. Add the date paste and sultanas. Bind with the well-beaten egg and stir in the apple purée.

Grease and flour an 18 cm (7 inch) diameter tin and pour in the mixture. Bake in a preheated oven (gas 4/350°F/180°C) for 35 minutes until firm to the touch.

Makes 18 slices. Each slice is 10 g CHO. 60 kcals.

Date Apple Crumble

Quick and easy. I often make a crumble to serve hot with a meal then use the remainder as a cake the next day, served cold either by itself, or with ice cream.

Crumble
100 g (4 oz) wholewheat flour
25 g (1 oz) bran
25 g (1 oz) sesame seeds
50 g (2 oz) margarine

Filling
3 fair sized eating apples,
    weighing 375 g (13 oz)
75 g (3 oz) dried dates
150 ml (5 fl oz) water
1 tsp cinnamon
½ tsp mixed spices

To make the crumble topping: mix flour, bran and sesame seeds together. Rub in the margarine well. Put crumble mixture aside while making the filling.

Slice the apples thinly. Put the dates and water in a pan over a low heat and cook until a runny paste is formed (purée in a blender if still lumpy). Add the spices and sliced apple to the date mixture. If it seems a bit dry, add a couple of tablespoons of water to the mixture to moisten it.

Spoon into a 20–23 cm (8–9 inch) diameter baking tin and sprinkle crumble mixture evenly over the top. Bake in a preheated oven (gas 4/350°F/180°C) for 30–35 minutes until browned. Serve hot or cold.

Makes 16 slices. Each slice is 10 g CHO. 75 kcals.

Apple and Blackberry Crumble

Crumble
100 g (4 oz) wholewheat flour
25 g (1 oz) bran
25 g (1 oz) sesame seeds
50 g (2 oz) margarine

Filling
150 g (5 oz) blackberries
3 fair-sized eating apples,
    weighing 375 g (13 oz),
    thinly sliced
50 g (2 oz) ground almonds
1 tsp cinnamon

Prepare the crumble topping as in date apple crumble, above. Spread the blackberries over the bottom of a 20 cm (8 inch) square or round tin. Put the sliced apple over the blackberries. Mix the ground almonds with the cinnamon so that it becomes a brown colour and sprinkle evenly over the apples. Cover completely with the crumble topping.

Bake in a preheated oven (gas 4/350°F/180°C) for 30–35 minutes until it is browned on top and the juice is bubbling up the sides. Delicious served hot or cold.

Makes 12 slices. Each slice is 10 g CHO. 100 kcals.

Apple Crisp

This is a taste of contrasts, a very crispy topping with a soft satin-smooth filling.

Topping
50 g (2 oz) wholewheat flour
50 g (2 oz) brown rice flakes
25 ml (1 fl oz) oil
25 ml (1 fl oz) orange juice

Filling
50 g (2 oz) dried figs, soaked
  in 50 ml (2 fl oz) water for
  15 minutes and chopped
50 g (2 oz) stoned prunes
½ tsp ginger
1 tsp cinnamon
2 eating apples, weighing
  225 g (8 oz), grated

To make the topping, mix the flour and rice flakes together in a bowl. Bind with the oil and orange juice, stirring thoroughly to make sure liquids are well distributed.

Heat the figs and soaking water in a pan over a low heat, until all the water is absorbed and a mushy paste is formed. Grind the prunes (an electric coffee grinder is useful for such a small quantity) and add to the paste. Take off heat after about 30 seconds. Add the spices and grated apple.

Pour the filling evenly over the base of an 18 cm (7 inch) diameter pie tin and cover with the topping. Bake in a preheated oven (gas 4/350°F/180°C) for 30 minutes until browned on top.

Makes 7 large slices. Each slice is 20 g CHO. 120 kcals.

CHEESECAKES

Cheesecakes are traditionally made up of a crust with a cheese custard filling on top. The base is often sponge, crushed biscuits or a shortcrust pastry. Most of the recipes here use a specially created crust that is high in fibre and quick to make. Most people don't have the time to start making elaborate bases for a cheesecake, they want something quick and easy. There are also recipes using sweet pie crust pastry and yeast pastry. All cheesecakes are very suitable for decoration with fresh fruit, and if you use two or three different kinds of fruit you can create a really spectacular effect in your own kitchen.

Carob Feather Cheesecake

The feather decoration on this cake makes it very eye-catching.

Crust
15 g (½ oz) dried dates
25 ml (1 fl oz) water
50 ml (2 fl oz) skimmed milk
10 g (⅓ oz) carob powder
1 bar shredded wheat

Filling
1 egg, size 3, separated
250 g (9 oz) skimmed milk quark

75 g (3 oz) sultanas
1 tbls lemon juice
50 ml (2 fl oz) low-fat natural yoghurt

Topping
50 ml (2 fl oz) low-fat natural yoghurt
25 g (1 oz) carob powder

To make the crust: very lightly grease or oil an 18 cm (7 inch) diameter baking tin. Heat the dates with the water in a small pan. Add the milk and carob and stir until a thick paste is formed. Take off the heat. Crumble the shredded wheat into the carob mixture and stir until all the shredded wheat is coated and has turned dark brown. Pat this mixture evenly over the base of the tin.

Then make the filling. Beat the egg yolk well. Add the quark, sultanas, lemon juice and yoghurt. Beat the egg white until stiff then fold into the mixture. Pour the mixture evenly over the crust.

Combine the yogurt and carob into a stiff mixture. Using a teaspoon, spoon the carob mixture in lines across the top of the cake – four or five lines all going in the same direction. Use a knife to make a feathered effect by drawing lines across the surface of the cake in the opposite direction from the carob lines. Do not dig down too deeply with the knife while doing this or you will end up dividing the cake into sections.

Bake in a preheated oven (gas 4/350°F/180°C) for 30 minutes until the cake is firm around the edges. Avoid overcooking cheesecake because it does continue to set even when it is out of the oven.

Makes 12 small slices. Each slice is 10 g CHO. 60 kcals.

Cottage Cheesecake

This makes a light fruity cheesecake. As with all the cheesecakes, store in the fridge when cooled.

Crust
15 g (½ oz) dried dates
25 ml (1 fl oz) water
50 ml (2 fl oz) skimmed milk
10 g (⅓ oz) carob powder
1 bar shredded wheat

Filling
75 g (3 oz) dried dates, chopped
50 ml (2 fl oz) water

100 g (4 oz) low-fat cottage cheese
150 g (5 oz) skimmed milk quark
½ tsp vanilla
1 egg, size 3, separated
1 peach, peeled and chopped (if out of season use 50 g [2 oz] banana)

Prepare the crust as for carob feather cheesecake, above.

Heat the dates and water in a pan over a low heat until the water is absorbed and a paste is formed. It does not matter if a few irregular pieces remain as they add interest to the cake. Leave to cool.

Remove the lumps from the cottage cheese by using either a food processor, mouli or sieve. Add the quark cheese. Fold in the date paste. Beat the egg yolk well and add with the vanilla. Lightly fold in the chopped peach. Beat the egg white until stiff, then fold in.

Pour over the crust and bake in a preheated oven (gas 4/350°C/180°C) for 35–40 minutes until browned on top.

Makes 10 slices. Each slice is 10 g CHO. 65 kcals.

OPTIONAL TOPPING

This cake can be decorated with any fruit, such as peaches, cherries or strawberries. Remember to add their carbohydrate value to the cake's total. A glazed effect can be achieved by mixing 25 g (1 oz) sugar-free jam with 50 ml (2 fl oz) water. Let this bubble for a minute until thickened and then spoon over the fruit. If doing this with 100 g (4 oz) cherries the total carbohydrate value for the topping would be 20 g CHO and approximately 70 kcals.

Tofu Cheesecake

This is a milk-free, egg-free cake, ideal if you are a vegan – or just want to avoid eggs and dairy products. For nutritional purposes, the tofu contains much the same quantity of calcium as the equivalent quantity of skimmed milk.

Filling	Crust
350 g (12 oz) firm tofu	15 g ($\frac{1}{2}$ oz) dried dates
60 g ($2\frac{1}{2}$ oz) dried dates	50 ml (2 fl oz) water
200 g (7 oz) bananas	15 g ($\frac{1}{2}$ oz) carob
2 tsp vanilla	powder
1 tbls lemon juice	50 ml (2 fl oz) unsweetened
25 g (1 oz) ground walnuts	orange juice
	1$\frac{1}{2}$ bars shredded wheat

The best way to make the filling is to use a food processor or liquidizer, but a mouli can be used instead to blend the tofu and bananas into a creamy paste. When using a food processor, blend the tofu first. Then add dates, and finally the bananas until the mixture becomes very creamy. Add the vanilla, lemon juice and ground walnuts. (If using a mouli, you will need to heat the dates with 50 ml (2 fl oz) water until a thick paste is formed. Add to the tofu and bananas with the other ingredients.)

To make the crust, gently heat the dates and water in a saucepan until a runny paste forms. Add the carob powder and orange juice. Take it off the heat, allow to cool for a couple of minutes and add the shredded wheat, crumbling it in with your fingers. Stir until all the shredded wheat is coated with carob sauce. Press into a 20 cm (8 inch) diameter greased tin, patting the soft mixture with the flat of your finger tips so that it is distributed over the whole tin.

Spoon the filling over the crust evenly and bake in a preheated oven (gas 4/350°F/180°C) for 35–40 minutes until the mixture becomes firm and a knife comes out cleanly. The filling will have the colour of *café au lait* and looks very attractive on the dark brown base. It can be decorated with sliced strawberries (150 g=10 g CHO) or any other soft fruit in season (but remember to include any added fruit in the cake's total carbohydrate value).

Makes 12 slices. Each slice is 10 g CHO. 70 kcals.

Pumpkin Cheesecake

This is a light, fragrant cake.

Filling
350 g (12 oz) cooked, mashed
   pumpkin (see recipe)
75 g (3 oz) dried dates
75 ml (3 fl oz) water
350 g (12 oz) skimmed milk quark
40 g (1½ oz) sultanas
1½ tsp grated orange rind
1½ tsp cinnamon
½ tsp ground ginger
¼ tsp ground cloves
sprinkling of grated nutmeg
1 tsp vanilla
1 egg, size 3

Crust
15 g (½ oz) dried dates
15 g (½ oz) carob powder
25 ml (1 fl oz) water
50 ml (2 fl oz) skimmed milk
1½ bars shredded wheat

To obtain 350 g (12 oz) cooked pumpkin you will need to cook rather more. Try double the weight you need, but this is only a rough guide as each pumpkin varies. Cut out the seeds and the pulp around them to prepare for cooking. Slice the pumpkin into large chunks, each with a piece of rind at its base. Stand in a little water in a saucepan and steam until the pumpkin is soft, adding more water if necessary, but make sure all the water has evaporated before you remove the pumpkin chunks. Peel off the rind and mash.

To make filling, cook the dates in the water over a low heat until a thick paste forms. Blend to make it really smooth. Leave to cool. Combine the mashed pumpkin and quark. Add the sultanas, date paste, orange rind, spices and vanilla. Whisk the egg well and fold in.

To make the crust, heat the dates, carob powder and water over a low heat until a paste is formed. You will need to stir this while it is in the pan. Add milk to make the consistency more liquid. Let the mixture bubble for a few seconds only, then remove from heat. Crumble shredded wheat into the mixture and stir until well coated. Pat evenly over the base of a 20 cm (8 inch) square greased tin.

Pour in the filling and bake in a preheated oven (gas 4/350°F/180°C) for 1 hour or until a knife comes out cleanly.

Makes 14 slices. Each slice is 10 g CHO. 60 kcals.

Apple Cheesecake

In this recipe you make an apple jelly which is added to the cheeses and allowed to go firm overnight in the fridge. This is helped by using a vegetarian setting agent called agar-agar. Unlike gelatine, which comes from animal bones, agar-agar is a type of seaweed. (If you want to experiment with seaweed in your food, see the recipe for oat and seaweed griddle cakes, p. 96). If the apples have not been sprayed include the peel, otherwise peel them. This recipe gives a larger than usual size cake.

1 quantity sweet pie crust (p. 70)

Filling
2 medium eating apples,
  weighing 275 g (10 oz)
150 ml (6 fl oz) water
50 g (2 oz) dried dates
1 tbls agar-agar flakes

100 ml (4 fl oz) unsweeetened
  apple juice
1 egg, size 3, separated
1 tsp cinnamon
250 g (9 oz) skimmed milk
  quark
150 g (5 oz) cottage cheese,
  sieved or blended

Pat the pastry around the base of a 23 cm (9 inch) diameter tin or deep dish. Bake in a preheated oven (gas 4/350°F/180°C) for 20 minutes until the pastry is cooked and just beginning to brown at the edges. Leave to cool while preparing the filling.

To make filling, slice the apples and put in a pan with chopped dates and 150 ml (6 fl oz) water over a low heat until the fruit becomes soft. Blend to make a smooth paste.

Return to the pan and add the agar-agar and apple juice. Slowly bring to the boil and allow to bubble gently for 5 minutes. Take off the heat and allow to cool.

Whisk the egg yolk and gradually add the cooled apple and date jelly to the beaten yolk. (Do wait until the jelly has cooled or you are likely to have fried egg in the jelly!) Add the cinnamon. Combine the quark and sieved cottage cheese. Fold in the jelly mixture and stir well. Finally, beat the egg white until stiff and fold in.

Pour the mixture over the cold pie crust and leave to stand in the fridge overnight. To make this cake more festive you can decorate it with slivers of fruit, just remember to add their carbohydrate value on to the cake's total.

Makes 12 large slices. Each slice is 10 g CHO. 100 kcals.

Pastry Cheesecake

½ quantity yeast pastry (p. 66)	50 g (2 oz) low-fat cottage cheese
Filling	½ well beaten egg, size 3
75 g (3 oz) seedless raisins, soaked in 50 ml (2 fl oz) water for 15 minutes	1 tsp vanilla
	1 generous tsp grated lemon rind
175 g (6 oz) skimmed milk quark	25 g (1 oz) sugar-free apricot jam

Boil the raisins in their soaking water until it has all been absorbed.

Roll out the pastry thinly into a rectangle, but not so thin that if it stretches it goes into holes – in this recipe the yeast pastry needs to be firm. Transfer to a baking tray (this is to avoid having to lift it up with the filling inside – which could have messy results!)

Mix the quark, cottage cheese and raisins together. Fold in the egg, vanilla and lemon rind.

Spread the jam over the centre third of the pastry, then spread the filling over the jam. Fold the two outer flaps over, envelope style, and seal the ends by folding these over as well. The purpose of this secure folding is to prevent the filling oozing out. (Another easier way of doing this is to use an 18 cm (7 inch) diameter tin, cut out a top and bottom from the pastry for the tin, and put the filling between the two layers. This does not give the traditional shape but is less fiddly.)

Leave to rise for 20 minutes. Brush the top with a little skimmed milk. Bake in a preheated oven (gas 4/350°F/180°C) for 35–40 minutes.

Makes 12 slices. Each slice is 10 g CHO. 75 kcals.

CARROT CAKES

Carrot might sound a surprising ingredient for use in cakes but it is a naturally sweet and wholesome vegetable and makes cakes meltingly moist. Its use in cakes was encouraged by government propaganda during the Second World War because of food shortages, prompting one cookery writer to protest that 'it is a tortuous path from fresh, crisp raw carrot to carrot flan, and I, for one, don't want to travel it.' Now that we no longer live in a period of austerity, modern carrot cakes can combine carrots with a wide variety of other ingredients, so that the carrot taste does not dominate but blends with all the flavours.

Nutritionally, carrots are, as you would imagine, high in carotene (vitamin A). They contain many minerals, vitamin C, a little vitamin E and small amounts of the B vitamins. If you buy organically grown carrots do not peel them as you will be removing fibre. Scrub clean with a brush and then grate.

Carrot Fruit Cake

The actual mixing of this cake takes very little time – preparing all the ingredients can make it quite lengthy. But its sweet, spicy flavour makes the labour well worthwhile.

75 g (3 oz) wholewheat flour
50 g (2 oz) millet flakes
1 tsp bicarbonate of soda
2 tsp cream of tartar
1 tsp cinnamon
½ tsp ground ginger
¼ tsp ground cloves
a little grated nutmeg
50 g (2 oz) stoned prunes

50 g (2 oz) dried apricots
200 g (7 oz) carrots, finely
    grated
50 g (2 oz) sultanas
25 ml (1 fl oz) oil
1 egg, size 3
1 tsp grated lemon rind
1 tsp grated orange rind
25 g (1 oz) chopped walnuts

Mix together the flour, millet flakes, bicarbonate of soda, cream of tartar, and spices. Finely grind the prunes and apricots – I use the coffee grinder attachment to my liquidizer for this. Add to the mixture with the carrots and sultanas. Stir oil into this mixture. Beat the egg well and add to the mixture. Finally fold in the grated rinds and chopped walnuts.

Pour into a greased and floured tin; an angel cake tin with a

hole in the middle is ideal for this kind of ca[...]
preheated oven (gas 4/350°C/180°C) for 45 minutes.

Makes 16 small slices. Each slice is 10 g CHO. 75 kcals.

Carrot-Coconut Cake

Here is carrot in yet another guise. Unlike the other recipes in this section, where the carrot blends with the other ingredients, you can identify the grated carrot together with the grated apple and coconut. This makes a varied moist texture. But do make sure that you grate the carrots finely.

50 g (2 oz) dried dates	1 apple, finely grated
50 ml (2 fl oz) water	1 tsp cinnamon
25 g (1 oz) sultanas, chopped in half	1 tsp vanilla
	1 egg, size 3
150 g (5 oz) carrots, finely grated	50 g (2 oz) porridge oats
50 g (2 oz) unsweetened desiccated coconut	75 g (3 oz) wholewheat flour
	100 ml (4 fl oz) skimmed milk

Cook the dates in the water over a low heat until a paste is formed. Work in a blender to make a smooth paste. Then leave until cool. Add the sultanas to the date paste.

In a large bowl mix the grated carrot, coconut, grated apple, cinnamon and vanilla. Combine with the date and sultana paste. Beat the egg well so that it begins to turn creamy and add. Stir in the oats, flour and milk to make a moist mixture.

Pour into a 20 cm (8 inch) square greased and floured tin and bake in a preheated oven (gas 4/350°F/180°C) for 40–45 minutes until the cake is well browned and firm to the touch.

Makes 16 squares. Each square is 10 g CHO. 70 kcals.

Carob Carrot Cake

Another way to enhance the sweetness of carrots is by combining them with carob. Carob is a naturally sweet alternative to chocolate. Unlike chocolate it has a very low fat content and is not likely to cause allergic reactions in the susceptible. An added bonus compared to chocolate is that it has a lower calorie count and is high in fibre.

75 g (3 oz) dried dates
75 ml (3 fl oz) water
75 g (3 oz) wholewheat flour
40 g (1½ oz) millet flakes
25 g (1 oz) carob powder
25 g (1 oz) ground walnuts
1 tsp bicarbonate of soda
2 tsp cream of tartar

1 tsp cinnamon
25 ml (1 fl oz) oil
1 egg, size 3, well beaten
200 g (7 oz) carrots, finely
    grated
1 dessertspoon finely grated
    lemon rind
1 tsp vanilla

Cook the dates with the water in a small pan over a low heat. As you mash the dates into the water with a spoon, a thick paste will form. Cook gently for a few minutes until all the water is absorbed. If necessary, blend to get a paste-like consistency. Leave until cool.

Mix together the flour, millet flakes, carob, ground walnuts, bicarbonate of soda, cream of tartar and cinnamon. Stir in the oil and well-beaten egg. Finally add the date paste, grated carrots, lemon rind and vanilla. Make sure that you stir the carrot in well so that the whole mixture is a dark brown colour and a fairly heavy consistency.

Cook in a greased and floured angel cake tin in a moderate oven (gas 4/350°F/180°C) for 50–60 minutes until a knife inserted into the centre comes out cleanly and the sides of the cake come away from the tin.

Makes 14 slices. Each slice is 10 g CHO. 80 kcals.

Suggested topping: apricot cream icing (p. 114).

Carrot-Banana Squares

These are moist and fruity squares. This recipe is egg-free which makes it useful for anyone trying to keep down the number of eggs in their diet.

75 g (3 oz) wholewheat flour
90 g (3½ oz) cooked brown rice
    (30 g [just over 1 oz] uncooked
    brown rice)
50 g (2 oz) bran
1 tsp mixed spice
1 tsp bicarbonate of soda
2 tsp cream of tartar

200 g (7 oz) banana, mashed
200 g (7 oz) carrots, grated
    finely
75 g (3 oz) sultanas
150 ml (5 fl oz) low-fat natural
    yogurt
1 tsp sesame seeds (optional)

Mix together the flour, cooked rice, bran, spice, bicarbonate of soda and cream of tartar. Add the mashed banana and finely grated carrot. (If the carrot is not very finely grated, you will become aware of carrot pieces in the cake.) Fold in the sultanas and bind with the yogurt.

Pour the mixture into a greased and floured 20 cm (8 inch) square tin. For an interesting finish sprinkle the top of the mixture with a teaspoon of sesame seeds. Bake in a preheated oven (gas 4/350°F/180°C) for 45–55 minutes until it is browned on top and firm. Cut into 16 squares when cool.

Makes 16 squares. Each square is 10 g CHO. 60 kcals.

Carrot-Chestnut Cake

75 g (3 oz) dried dates
75 ml (3 fl oz) water
150 g (5 oz) unsweetened
    chestnut purée*
150 g (5 oz) carrots, finely grated
2 eggs, size 3

75 g (3 oz) wholewheat flour
50 g (2 oz) millet flakes
15 g ($\frac{1}{2}$ oz) bran
1 tsp cream of tartar
$\frac{1}{2}$ tsp bicarbonate of soda
$\frac{1}{2}$ tsp vanilla

Put the dates and water in a pan over a low heat and cook until all the water is absorbed. Leave until cool. Work in the blender to make an even smooth paste. Mix the chestnut purée with the grated carrots and add to the date paste. Beat the eggs well until they become creamy; this is an effective way of making the cake lighter and airier. Add to the mixture then fold in the combined flour, millet flakes, bran, cream of tartar and bicarbonate of soda. Add the vanilla.

Pour into a greased and floured 20 cm (8 inch) diameter baking tin. Bake in a preheated oven (gas 4/350°F/180°C) for 40 minutes until firm to the touch and a knife inserted in the centre comes out cleanly.

Makes 20 small slices. Each slice is 10 g CHO. 55 kcals.

Unsweetened chestnut purée can be bought in a can. This is the quickest method. Any chestnut purée left over can be used for nut pastry (p. 62) and frozen, or to make chestnut tarts (p. 52). A lengthier but more precise method is to use fresh chestnuts. After peeling, boil them until soft and all cooking water is absorbed, then sieve or mouli. Out of season it is possible to obtain dried chestnuts but these have to be boiled for a considerable length of time.

SPICE CAKES

Carob Cake

This is a very light moist cake. It also works well if baked in paper cases to make cupcakes and decorated with coconut cream icing (p. 114). If you feel like something more luscious use one of the carob icing recipes (pp. 112–13). (Remember to add the carbohydrate and calorie value of the icing on to the cake.)

90 g (3½ oz) dried dates
75 ml (3 fl oz) water
100 g (4 oz) wholewheat flour
25 g (1 oz) low-fat soya flour
50 g (2 oz) carob powder
1 tsp bicarbonate of soda

2 tsp cream of tartar
50 g (2 oz) margarine
2 eggs, size 3
150 ml (5 fl oz) natural low-fat
    yogurt

Cook the dates in the water on a low heat until all the water has been absorbed by the dates and a thick paste has formed. Blend to make it really smooth. Leave until cool.

Mix together in a bowl the wholewheat and soya flours, carob powder, bicarbonate of soda and cream of tartar. Rub in the margarine – this is easy to do as the polyunsaturated margarines are very soft. Add the date paste to the flours. Whisk the eggs well until creamy; beating a lot of air into the eggs helps to make this cake so light. Fold in the eggs, then add the yogurt to give a mixture with a thick consistency.

Pour into a greased and floured 20 cm (8 inch) diameter tin and bake in a preheated oven (gas 4/350°F/180°C) for 30–35 minutes until a knife comes out cleanly from the middle. (Cupcakes will take 20–25 minutes.) Cool before decorating.

Makes 16 slices. Each slice is 10 g CHO. 75 kcals.

Spice Cake

This is a variation of the carob cake recipe. It substitutes fragrant spices for the carob powder.

115 g (4½ oz) dried dates
100 ml (4 fl oz) water
115 g (4½ oz) wholewheat flour

1½ tsp ground ginger
2 tsp mixed spice
50 g (2 oz) margarine

25 g (1 oz) low-fat soya flour
1 tsp bicarbonate of soda
1 tsp cream of tartar
2 tsp cinnamon

2 eggs, size 3
150 ml (5 fl oz) low-fat natural
   yogurt
flaked almonds (optional)

Make a date paste as in carob cake, above. Mix the flours, bicarbonate of soda, cream of tartar and spices, then proceed as for carob cake. You can sprinkle the top of the cake with a few flaked almonds. Cook at gas 4/350°F/180°C for 30–35 minutes.

Makes 16 slices. Each slice is 10 g CHO. 85 kcals.

Spice Cake with Banana Filling

1 quantity spice cake mixture
   (opposite)
100 g (4 oz) banana

50 g (2 oz) firm tofu or cottage
cheese

Mash the banana. Sieve the tofu or cottage cheese, or work in a mouli, and add to the fruit mixture. Pour half the spice cake mixture into an angel cake tin. Spoon the filling evenly over the middle of the cake. Carefully spoon the remaining spice cake mixture on top and bake in a preheated oven (gas 4/350°F/180°C) for 30–35 minutes.

Makes 10 large slices. Each slice is 20 g CHO. 150 kcals.

Yogurt Walnut Cake

100 g (4 oz) dried dates
100 ml (4 fl oz) water
150 g (5 oz) wholewheat flour
25 g (1 oz) low-fat soya flour
25 g (1 oz) ground almonds
1 tsp bicarbonate of soda
2 tsp cream of tartar
1 tsp vanilla
2 eggs, size 3, well beaten
300 ml (10 fl oz) low-fat natural
   yogurt

Filling
25 g (1 oz) wheat germ
25 g (1 oz) unsweetened
   desiccated coconut
25 g (1 oz) chopped walnuts
3 tsp cinnamon
50 ml (2 fl oz) skimmed milk

Put the dates and water in a pan over a low heat until all the water is absorbed. Blend to make a smooth paste then leave until cool.

Combine the flours, ground almonds, bicarbonate of soda and cream of tartar. Add the cooled dates, vanilla and well-beaten eggs. Fold in the yogurt to make a soft mixture.

Mix all the filling ingredients together.

This cake works well in a 20 cm (8 inch) round tin or an angel cake tin. Grease and flour the tin you are using. Spoon just under half the cake mixture into the tin, spreading it around evenly. Spoon the filling evenly over the surface then put the remaining cake mixture on top of the filling. This is quite tricky to do without lifting the filling up. The best way is to spoon the mixture over the filling starting from the outside and working inwards.

Bake in a preheated oven (gas 4/350°F/180°C) for 45–50 minutes until a knife inserted in the centre comes out cleanly.

Suggested topping: coconut cream icing (p. 114).

Makes 20 small slices. Each slice is 10 g CHO. 80 kcals (90 with icing).

SEED AND DRIED FRUIT CAKES

Poppy Seed Cake

Poppy seed is used in cakes in Poland and other East European countries, but in Britain it is mainly used to decorate loaves of bread. The poppy seeds have a nut-like taste when ground down and mixed with sweet dried fruit.

This recipe is based on one given to me many years ago by Evelyn, who was teaching English in Nazareth. She was everything that you expect an overseas English teacher to be. Driving to her home one weekend she suggested we pass the time with a sing-song. I found myself joining in hearty renderings of 'Nymphs and Shepherds' and 'Blow the Wind Southerly' as we sped past the harsh arid countryside. I don't know how she came to have this outlandish recipe, perhaps from a neighbour, but it was the only thing about her that was out of English character.

100 g (4 oz) dried dates
100 ml (4 fl oz) water
75 g (3 oz) stoned prunes
50 ml (2 fl oz) oil
150 g (5 oz) poppy seeds, ground
2 eggs, size 3, separated

50 g (2 oz) wholewheat flour
25 ml (1 fl oz) skimmed milk
25 ml (1 fl oz) unsweetened orange juice
1 teaspoon rum essence or rum

Put the dates and water in a small pan and cook over a low heat until a thick paste is formed. Leave until cool.

Put the prunes in an electric coffee grinder and grind down until reduced to tiny pieces.

Combine the date paste, ground prunes and oil. Add the ground poppy seeds. (Either an electric coffee grinder or food processor can be used for this. Do not overlook this stage because if you were to put the poppy seeds in unground the cake would not have such a smooth texture.) Beat the egg yolks until they are creamy and add to the mixture. Add the flour, followed by the milk, orange juice and rum.

Whisk the egg whites until stiff and fold into the poppy seed mixture. Pour into a greased and floured 20 cm (8 inch) diameter baking tin. Bake in a preheated oven (gas 4/350°F/180°C) for 30–35 minutes until a knife inserted in the centre comes out cleanly.

A thick carob fudge icing (p. 112) goes very well with this cake – remember to add on the carbohydrate value if you use it.

Makes 16 slices. Each slice is 10 g CHO. 125 kcals.

Apple Sultana Cake

The ground almonds used in this recipe impart some of their own sweetness to this cake which together with the apples and sultanas makes it quite luscious. Almonds have one of the highest fibre contents of all nuts, and serve as a good source of protein. They are rich in calcium and phosphorus. This is a quick cake to make.

For special occasions it goes very well with coconut cream icing (p. 114)–try a pink carnation on top for a sensational effect.

75 g (3 oz) wholewheat flour	$\frac{1}{8}$ tsp ground cloves
25 g (1 oz) low-fat soya flour	$\frac{1}{8}$ tsp grated nutmeg
75 g (3 oz) ground almonds	100 g (4 oz) sultanas
25 g (1 oz) wheat germ	3 eating apples, weighing
$\frac{1}{2}$ tsp bicarbonate of soda	325 g (11$\frac{1}{2}$ oz), grated
1 tsp cream of tartar	1 egg white, stiffly beaten
1$\frac{1}{2}$ tsp cinnamon	

Mix the flours, ground almonds, wheat germ, bicarbonate of soda, cream of tartar and spices. Add the sultanas and grated apple. Mix in well with the flours. Bind with the stiffly beaten egg white. Pour into a lightly greased and floured 20 cm (8 inch) tin and bake in a preheated oven (gas 4/350°F/180°C) for 30–35 minutes until a knife comes out cleanly.

Makes 16 slices. Each slice is 10 g CHO. 75 kcals.

Date and Apricot Cake

The ground walnuts give this cake quite an unusual taste but it is the kind of unusual taste that has people coming back for more. Walnuts are high in polyunsaturated oils.

75 g (3 oz) wholewheat flour	100 g (4 oz) dried dates,
25 g (1 oz) low-fat soya flour	soaked in 50 ml (2 fl oz)
75 g (3 oz) ground walnuts	water for 30 minutes

25 g (1 oz) wheat germ
1 tsp cinnamon
1 tsp cream of tartar
1 tsp bicarbonate of soda
grated rind and juice of $\frac{1}{2}$ lemon

75 g (3 oz) dried apricots,
soaked in 50 ml (2 fl oz)
water for 30 minutes
1 egg, size 3, well beaten
150 ml (5 fl oz) low-fat natural
yogurt

Mix the flours, ground walnuts, wheat germ, cinnamon, cream of tartar, bicarbonate of soda, lemon rind and juice. Chop the dates and apricots well and boil them in their soaking water until it has all been absorbed. Cool and add to the flour. Fold in the well-beaten egg. Use a metal or wooden spoon to stir in the yogurt to make a smooth textured mixture.

Pour into a lightly greased and floured 20 cm (8 inch) square tin. Bake in a preheated oven (gas 4/350°F/180°C) for 30 minutes until the cake is browned on top and a knife inserted in the centre comes out cleanly.

Makes 16 slices. Each slice is 10 g CHO. 85 kcals.

Suggested topping: Coconut cream icing (p. 114).

Wholewheat Pasta Cake

This recipe is based on a traditional noodle recipe. It can be eaten hot or cold. I have tried the recipe with all the different shapes that pasta comes in – shells, rings, tubes and twirly spirals – but the very best shape is the short thin noodles sometimes called tagliatelle, not quite as frail as vermicelli, but one stage on. These strands stick together during the cooking and give a firm density to the cake. I often make this for tea on a Friday afternoon and the fragrant smell of cinnamon in the oven has come to mark the end of the week for us.

150 g (5 oz) wholewheat pasta
1 egg, size 3
1–2 tsp cinnamon
50 g (2 oz) sultanas
1 large eating apple, weighing
175 g (6 oz), grated (if

peaches are in season,
ring the changes by using
$\frac{1}{2}$ grated apple and $\frac{1}{2}$
grated peach)
50 ml (2 fl oz) unsweetened
orange juice

Cook the pasta in boiling water. Rinse thoroughly with cold

water and leave to stand in a colander so that the remaining water drips off. Whisk the egg. Stir in the cinnamon, sultanas and grated fruit. Gently fold in the pasta and orange juice. (This recipe can be prepared a few hours in advance and left to stand in the fridge without any detrimental effect.)

Pour ½ tsp oil into a 2 cm (8 inch) square baking dish and put this in the oven to become hot. Take the dish out and pour in the pasta mixture. Return to the preheated oven (gas 4/350°F/180°C) to cook for 30–35 minutes until it is browned on top. Serve hot or cold.

Makes 8 large slices. Each slice is 20 g CHO. 100 kcals.

Trifle

The life of sugar-free cakes is shorter than cakes with sugar and a recipe for trifle, using up leftover cake, comes in handy if you want to serve something for tea but think your cake is no longer as fresh as it should be. The trifle is best eaten within a day of being made. This recipe includes alternative fruit mixtures to go in the trifle and an apple jelly to pour over the fruit and cake. It is topped with a cream icing.

Base
½ cake (using one of the recipes in this book. An average half cake is about 80 g CHO, but check the specific recipe to be sure about this and the calorie content)

100 ml (4 fl oz) skimmed milk
1 tbls sherry or brandy
  (optional)

Different fruit toppings
275 g (10 oz) eating apples (sliced and lightly simmered with 1 tbls water)
50 g (2 oz) bananas
or
375 g (13 oz) strawberries
50 g (2 oz) bananas
or

325 g (11½ oz) pears (sliced into chunks and simmered with 1 tbls water)
75 g (3 oz) grapes (seeded and halved)
or
300 g (11 oz) ripe peaches, sliced
100 g (4 oz) cherries (stoned and halved)

Apple jelly
1 medium eating apple
100 ml (4 fl oz) apple juice
1 tsp agar-agar

Topping
double quantity apricot
    cream icing (p. 114)
flaked almonds, grated
    walnuts or apple flakes

Cut the cake into large pieces and put in the bottom of a bowl or deep dish. Mix the milk and sherry and pour over the cake to moisten it.

Choose a suitable fruit topping for the time of the year. Prepare and pour it over the moistened cake.

To make the apple jelly, slowly cook the sliced apple with a little water until it becomes soft. Blend or purée and add the apple juice. Pour this mixture into a measuring jug and add enough water to make the total quantity up to 250 ml (9 fl oz). Pour the watered-down purée into a small pan and add the agar-agar. Slowly bring to the boil and simmer gently for 5–6 minutes. Pour the jelly over the cake and fruit and allow to set.

When the jelly is firm, cover with apricot cream icing and sprinkle a few nuts or apple flakes over the top for decoration.

The total carbohydrate count for the fruit topping, jelly and cream is 80 g CHO. 480 kcals. If the cake used had 80 g CHO then together with the fruit topping, jelly and cream the trifle can make 8 large slices, each one 20 g CHO. 140 kcals.

PASTRIES AND BISCUITS

PASTRY

Pastry is an indispensable part of everyone's cooking repertoire. A good pastry can serve as a base for desserts and savoury dishes, for tartlets at teatime or pies for supper. This section contains five basic pastries, some simpler than others.

Whatever pastry you make, remember not to overwork it or to use too much liquid when binding. This is just as important when making pastry with wholewheat flour and with a low fat content. If you are using margarine, rub it in thoroughly but lightly; when adding liquid pour in just enough to make a crumbly mixture. As you work it into a dough your hands will quickly discover if it is too dry and needs additional moistening.

You can fill pastry with whatever you fancy: the options are infinite. In this section I include a few exotic fillings as well as many old favourites adapted to tasty sugar-free use. To help you adapt other recipes of your choice, I have given the carbohydrate value of each pastry after the recipe. If, for example, you combine the rough puff pastry which has 100 g CHO with your own filling of, say, 100 g CHO, the total carbohydrate count will be 200 g CHO. Twenty slices will make each individual slice equal to 10 g CHO.

When baking rolls of pastry or strudel, mark off slices before putting the pastry in the oven (see p. 21 for how to make one slice equal 10 g CHO). The marks will remain during baking and freezing.

The pastries keep well for a couple of days. After that they tend to dry up because they do not include sugar, which acts as a preservative. The basic pastries can also be prepared for use the next day if wrapped in foil and kept overnight in the fridge.

All the pastries and biscuits freeze well. Wrap them in foil or cling film and then in a freezer bag. Raw pastry keeps for up to 1 month, cooked biscuits and cooked pastry for up to 3 months. When freezing, write a label with details of what you have frozen and its carbohydrate and calorie content.

Do not grease your baking sheets unless specified by the recipe. All my pastry recipes contain some oil or margarine and this usually eliminates the need for greasing.

Quick Wholewheat Pastry

This is a very simple recipe and takes no more than five minutes to make. The pastry, when baked, is crisp. It is not as light or as supple as the wholewheat rough puff pastry and is best used for tarts or pie crusts, but it is less fiddly to make and has a low fat content. It can be used with any of the fillings given in this chapter – especially delicious are the fillings used in flaky apple pie (p. 54), black cherry strudel (p. 55), pumpkin pie (p. 61), tropical pie (p. 61) and velvet plum cake (p. 69).

200 g (7 oz) wholewheat flour   1 tbls lemon juice
25 ml (1 fl oz) oil   50–100 ml (2–4 fl oz) cold
                                                         water

Put the flour in a bowl. Stir in the oil and lemon juice with a knife or wooden spoon. Add just enough water to make thick crumbs which you can work into a soft pastry dough with your hands. This pastry should not be overworked, so do not knead it more than you have to.
   Chill in the fridge for 30 minutes. When rolling it out, sprinkle the board lightly with flour and roll out the pastry as thin as you can manage.

Total pastry is 130 g CHO. 860 kcals.

Jam Tarts

1 quantity quick wholewheat   200 g (7 oz) sugar-free jam
   pastry (above)

Roll out the pastry as thin as it will go, so that you can cut 32 × 6 cm (2½ inch) circles. Put the circles of pastry in jam tart tins. Fill with jam, spooning a little hot water over it to stop the jam drying out, and bake in a preheated oven (gas 5/375°F/190°C) for 15–20 minutes until the edges of the tarts are browned.

Makes 32 tarts. 3 tarts are 20 g CHO. 105 kcals.

Chestnut Tarts

100 g (4 oz) unsweetened
   chestnut purée (see p. 41 for
   notes on chestnut purée)
100 g (4 oz) skimmed milk quark
25 ml (1 fl oz) boiling water

30 g (generous 1 oz) dried
   dates, finely chopped

½ quantity quick wholewheat
   pastry (p. 51)

Mix together the chestnut purée and quark. Pour the boiling water over the finely chopped dates to make a paste. Cool and add to the chestnut and quark mixture.

Roll out the pastry as thinly as possible and cut out 16 × 6 cm (2½ inch) circles. Bake these blind in jam tart tins in a preheated oven (gas 5/375°F/190°C) for 10–15 minutes until browned. (The thinner they are the less time they will take.)

Remove the pastry cases from the tin and when cool fill with equal amounts of the chestnut filling. Decorate each tart with a thin sliver of dried date. Store in the fridge.

Makes 16 tarts. 2 tarts are 15 g CHO. 90 kcals.

Wholewheat Rough Puff Pastry

This recipe is based on the traditional method used for rough puff pastry but cuts down the high fat content. It is a supple pastry that can be rolled very thin and gives a light crisp result.

150 g (5 oz) wholewheat flour
50 g (2 oz) margarine

50–75 ml (2–3 fl oz) cold
   water

Put the flour in a bowl. Add the margarine and cut up loosely in the bowl so that it becomes coated with flour. Add enough water to bind the flour and margarine into a dry dough. Put the dough on a lightly floured board and roll it out in a narrow oblong about 25 × 10 cm (10 × 4 inches). At this stage not all the margarine will be evenly distributed in the dough. Mark the dough off lightly into three sections. Turn the top section over the second and fold the third over last of all (see diagram). Give the pastry a quarter turn and repeat, rolling out, folding into three and giving a quarter turn again. After about four times the margarine will have been rolled into the flour and the pastry will have an even colour and texture.

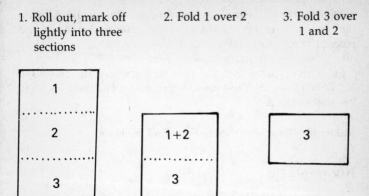

1. Roll out, mark off lightly into three sections

2. Fold 1 over 2

3. Fold 3 over 1 and 2

Chill in the fridge for 30 minutes. Roll out and fold into three once more before using.

Total pastry is 100 g CHO. 840 kcals.

Quick and Easy Apple Strudel

This is one of my family's favourites. The rough puff pastry acts as a useful substitute for strudel pastry in this sociable snack.

½ quantity wholewheat rough puff pastry (p. 52)

25 g (1 oz) sugar-free strawberry jam

2 medium eating apples, weighing 275 g (10 oz), grated

25 g (1 oz) ground almonds

1 tsp cinnamon

50 g (2 oz) sultanas

Roll pastry thinly into an oblong roughly 23 × 33 cm (9 × 13 inches). Use a little flour to roll out the pastry so that when you roll up the strudel you don't find it is stuck hard to the rolling board.

Spread the surface with strawberry jam, keeping a 1 cm (½ inch) margin round the edges. Imagine the pastry is divided into thirds lengthways. Spread the grated apple along the middle third of the pastry. Mix the ground almonds and cinnamon together to make a dark brown mixture and cover the apples with this. Sprinkle evenly with sultanas. Fold over the two outside pieces of pastry like an envelope. If necessary dampen the edge of the first piece with a drop of water so that the second piece of pastry seals firmly. Seal at both ends of the strudel. Mark off 12 slices on the strudel.

Place on a baking tray and cook in a preheated oven (gas 4/350°F/180°C) for 35–40 minutes so that the apple strudel cooks all the way through.

Makes 10 slices. Each slice is 10 g CHO. 80 kcals.

Flaky Apple Pie

Rough puff pastry is delicious eaten hot. The easiest way of serving it is as a pie. Use the same ingredients as in apple strudel, above, only substitute apricot sugar-free jam for the strawberry. Roll out a pastry top and bottom for a 20 cm (8 inch) tin. Fill the bottom pastry lining with grated apple. Cover with the ground almonds mixed with the cinnamon and sultanas. Dot the apricot jam over the ground almond mixture. Put on the pastry lid and sprinkle the top with cinnamon. Bake in a preheated oven (gas 5/375°F/190°C) for 25–30 minutes.

Makes 10 servings. Each serving is 10 g CHO. 80 kcals.

Carob Roll

Carob, unlike cocoa, is naturally sweet. It is an ancient food, originating in the Mediterranean area. The carob pod is also known as St John's bread or locust bread. Unlike cocoa, carob does not contain the stimulants caffeine or theobromine. It also has a much lower fat content – 100 grams carob powder contain 0.7 per cent fat as opposed to cocoa powder's 23.7 per cent. It can take time to get used to substituting the taste of carob for cocoa. This recipe, which combines a carob filling with a plain pastry, is a good starting point.

½ quantity wholewheat rough puff pastry (p. 52)

25 g (1 oz) sugar-free apricot jam
50 g (2 oz) ground almonds

25 g (1 oz) carob powder
50 g (2 oz) sultanas
½ orange or 50 ml (2 fl oz) orange juice

Roll the pastry thinly into an oblong about 23 × 33 cm (9 × 13 inches). Use a little flour to roll out the pastry so that when you roll it up it is not stuck hard to the rolling board.

Spread the surface with apricot jam, keeping a 1 cm (½ inch) margin around the edges. Mix the ground almonds with the carob and sultanas and spread over the jam. Peel the orange, chop finely and spread over the ground almond mixture. (If using orange juice mix it in with the ground almonds and carob.) Roll up swiss-roll style and seal at both ends. Mark off 12 slices.

Place on a baking tray and cook in a preheated oven (gas 4/ 350°F/180°C) for 30–35 minutes.

Makes 10 slices. Each slice is 10 g CHO. 95 kcals.

Black Cherry Strudel

The cherry season in Britain is normally a short one, but the season has been made longer by imports from America and Europe. Last summer there were so many cherries in the shops and markets that a friend bought me an amazing gadget called a cherry stoner. In a brief manoeuvre the stone is removed cleanly from the cherry. My daughters and their friends got great pleasure from both watching me perform this trick and eating the results. It seemed the right time to work out a recipe for cherry strudel.

½ quantity wholewheat rough puff pastry (p. 52)

25 g (1 oz) sugar-free black cherry jam

25 g (1 oz) ground almonds
1 tsp cinnamon
450 g (1 lb) black cherries, stoned and chopped
1 medium eating apple, grated

Roll out the pastry as for apple strudel (p. 53). Spread the surface with black cherry jam, keeping a 1 cm (½ inch) margin around the edges. Imagine that the pastry is divided into thirds lengthways. Spread the ground almonds and cinnamon, mixed together, over the middle third. Mix the cherries with the grated apple and spoon evenly over the almonds and cinnamon. Fold the two outer pieces of pastry over the top, envelope style. If necessary dampen the edge of the first piece with a drop of water so that the second piece of pastry seals firmly. Seal at both ends of the strudel. Mark off 10 slices on the strudel pastry.

Place on a baking sheet and cook in a preheated oven (gas 5/375°F/190°C) for 30–35 minutes.

Makes 10 large slices. Each slice is 10 g CHO. 80 kcals.

Poppy Seed Roll

Poppy seeds mixed with sweet fruit create a very special taste. (They also contain the B vitamins.)

½ quantity wholewheat rough puff pastry (p. 52)	50 ml (2 fl oz) water
	50 g (2 oz) poppy seeds, ground
25 g (1 oz) sugar-free apricot jam	50 ml (2 fl oz) skimmed milk
	15 g (½ oz) ground almonds
Poppy seed filling	15 g (½ oz) wheat germ
50 g (2 oz) stoned prunes	1 tsp vanilla
50 g (2 oz) dried figs, finely chopped	juice of ½ orange
	½ tsp grated orange rind

First prepare the filling. Grind the prunes finely (an electric coffee grinder is useful for such a small quantity). Put the figs and water in a pan over a low heat and mix until all the water is absorbed. Add the ground prunes and poppy seeds. Stir in the milk and when all the ingredients have mixed to a thick paste remove from the heat. Add the ground almonds, wheat germ, vanilla, orange juice and grated rind.

Roll out the pastry thinly, spread with jam and roll up swiss-roll style as in carob roll (p. 54). Mark off 12 slices on the roll. Bake in a preheated oven (gas 4/350°F/180°C) for 30–35 minutes.

Makes 12 slices. Each slice is 10 g CHO. 85 kcals.

Fruity Slices

These are very sweet biscuits made with dried fruit.

½ quantity wholewheat rough puff pastry (p. 52)	60 g (2½ oz) dried apricots
	50 g (2 oz) raisins, soaked in 50 ml (2 fl oz) water for 15 minutes
25 g (1 oz) sugar-free strawberry jam	25 ml (1 fl oz) apple juice
25 g (1 oz) dried dates	

Roll out the pastry thinly into a long oblong. Spread with the strawberry jam. Chop the dates and apricots and simmer with the raisins in the soaking water and apple juice until the liquid is absorbed. Take off the heat and leave to cool.

Spread the dried fruit mixture over the pastry leaving a margin around the edges. Roll up into a narrow roll and seal the ends.

Place on a baking sheet and bake in a preheated oven (gas 5/375°F/190°C) for 30 minutes until browned. The roll is marked up into 12 divisions, but biscuits are better if cut thinner, so when cooled cut the whole roll into 24 slices.

Makes 24 slices. 2 slices are 10 g CHO. 65 kcals.

Sesame Crescents

Sesame seeds are particularly high in calcium: 815 mg calcium per 100 grams, if the seeds have not been dehusked. Dehusked seeds contain only 110 mg. The way to tell the difference is that the sesame seeds which have not had their husks removed are dark brown, the dehusked seeds are lighter. It is unlikely that you would eat as much as 50 mg sesame seeds a day, but if you did you would have consumed almost the entire recommended daily calcium intake (500 mg).

1 quantity wholewheat rough puff pastry (p. 52)

75 g (3 oz) dried figs, chopped
50 ml (2 fl oz) water

25 g (1 oz) ground almonds
1 tsp cinnamon
½ tsp nutmeg
100 g (4 oz) sesame seeds

Cook the figs and water in a pan over a low heat until the water is absorbed and a mushy paste is formed. Blend if necessary. Cool. Add the ground almonds, cinnamon and nutmeg. Toast the sesame seeds under the grill or in the oven until browned and add.

Roll out the pastry thinly and make 32 circles using a 6 cm (2½ inch) cutter. Place the circles on a baking sheet.

Place an equal amount of filling in each one. Bring the two sides over to meet in the middle and pinch together to make a standing half circle. You may need to stretch the pastry a little to make the edges meet. Bake in a preheated oven (gas 5/375°F/190°C) for 20 minutes until browned.

Makes 32 crescents. 2 crescents are 10 g CHO. 110 kcals.

Date Crescents

Make these like the sesame crescents above but substitute the
date filling.

1 quantity wholewheat rough
   puff pastry (p. 52)

100 g (4 oz) dried dates,
   chopped
25 g (1 oz) prunes, stoned and
   chopped

50 ml (2 fl oz) unsweetened
   orange juice
50 ml (2 fl oz) water
1 tsp cinnamon
2 tsp lemon juice

Cook the dates, prunes, orange juice and water in a pan over a
low heat until all the liquid is absorbed and it becomes a mushy
paste. Blend if it needs to be smoother. Take off the heat and add
the cinnamon and lemon juice.

Roll out the pastry and cut 16 × 7.5 cm (3 inch) circles. Place the
circles on a baking sheet. Place an equal amount of filling in each
one Bring the two sides over to meet in the middle and pinch
together to make a standing half circle or crescent. Bake in a
preheated oven (gas 5/375°F/190°C) for 25 minutes until browned.

Makes 16 crescents. Each crescent is 10 g CHO. 70 kcals.

Apricot-Pumpkin Crescents

Pumpkin seeds and pumpkins are more normally associated with
Cinderella and her coach than gourmet eating. Seeds can be a
good source of many minerals. Once you have got used to the
taste of these seeds as part of a biscuit filling you will find that
they are an attractive nibble by themselves. Put them out on a
plate at the end of the meal or when you have guests. And it
takes 65 g (2½ oz) to make 10 g CHO, which is a lot of pumpkin
seeds!

75 g (3 oz) dried apricots
75 g (3 oz) pumpkin seeds

1 quantity wholewheat rough
   puff pastry (p. 52)

Prepare the filling: pour enough boiling water over the dried
apricots to cover them. Leave them to stand for at least 30

minutes and then simmer over a low heat until the water is absorbed. Work in the blender to make a smooth paste.

Chop the pumpkin seeds. (It is quicker to use a machine to do this than painstaking chopping by hand, although they will tend to reduce to powder very quickly. Try to avoid this by switching off the machine while they are still a bit coarse and some crunchy bits are left.) Mix with the apricot paste.

Roll out the pastry thinly and cut out 30 × 6 cm (2½ inch) circles. Fill the centre of each circle with a teaspoon of the apricot-pumpkin mixture. Bring the two sides over to meet in the middle and pinch together making a standing half circle, or crescent. Place on a baking sheet and cook in a preheated oven (gas 5/375°F/190°C) for 20–25 minutes until evenly browned.

Makes 30 biscuits. 2 are 10 g CHO. 45 kcals.

Aduki Tarts

Blended aduki beans mixed with dried figs make a sweet filling in a light pastry. It is also a gentle way of getting family or friends used to the idea of eating these red beans which are so favoured by diabetic dietary groups. Some call these small red beans the king of the beans. They are indigenous to the Far East and it takes some Europeans time and patience to acquire a taste for them. It is worth persisting: like all beans they are not only high in fibre and protein but are said to be beneficial to the kidneys.

1 quantity wholewheat rough
   puff pastry (p. 52)

100 g (4 oz) cooked aduki beans,
   blended (cook about 40 g [1½ oz]

dried aduki beans, see
   recipe)
65 g (2½ oz) dried figs
50 ml (2 fl oz) water

To prepare aduki beans: leave to soak overnight in cold water. Cooked in a pressure cooker they will take 10–15 minutes. Do not cook them in an excessive amount of water, so that when tender the remaining water can be boiled away. If using a saucepan, bring to the boil and then simmer over a low heat with the lid on until the beans are soft and the water is absorbed. Be careful not to burn them at this stage. This takes about 40 minutes. This is a lot of trouble to go to for just 40 g of aduki beans and it is advisable to cook up a larger amount and store them in your fridge. If you cover the beans they will keep for quite a few days and are handy to pop into savoury dishes.

Now prepare the figs. Chop the dried figs into a small pan and cook with the water over a low heat until all the water is absorbed. Blend to make a paste. Mix the fig paste with the blended aduki beans.

Roll out the pastry thinly into an oblong large enough to cut out 40 circles of 5 cm (2 inches) diameter. Place 20 of the circles into ungreased jam tart tins. Put a heaped teaspoon of the filling into each one. Cover the tarts with the remaining 20 circles and press together the sides of the tarts. (The filling is fairly solid and there is no worry of it oozing out at the sides.)

Bake in a preheated oven (gas 5/375°F/190°C) for 20 minutes or until evenly browned.

Makes 20 tarts. 3 tarts are 20 g CHO. 105 kcals.

Cottage Cheese Pastry

150 g (5 oz) wholewheat flour
½ tsp cinnamon

25 g (1 oz) margarine
150 g (5 oz) low-fat cottage cheese

Mix the flour and cinnamon. Rub in the margarine. Use the cottage cheese to bind this into a dough. If you are not using a mixer you will need to sieve or mouli the cottage cheese to get rid of the little lumps, before adding it to the flour and margarine. Chill in the fridge for 30 minutes before using.

Total pastry is 100 g CHO. 810 kcals.

Jam Hearts

1 quantity cottage cheese pastry
   (above)

50 g (2 oz) sugar-free strawberry jam
a little cinnamon

Roll the pastry out as thinly as possible on a lightly floured board. Use a 5 cm (2 inch) heart-shaped cutter to cut 30 shapes. Place half the hearts on a baking sheet. Spread with the jam. Put the remaining heart shapes on top to make a sandwich. Sprinkle the tops of the pastry with a pinch each of cinnamon. Bake in a preheated oven (gas 5/375°F/190°C) for 15 minutes.

Makes 15 biscuits. 2 biscuits are 15 g CHO. 120 kcals.

Pumpkin Pie

1 quantity cottage cheese pastry
  (p. 60)

150 g (5 oz) cooked pumpkin,
  mashed

75 g (3 oz) dried figs
75 ml (3 fl oz) water
1 dessertspoon lemon juice

Prepare the pumpkin as for pumpkin cheesecake (p. 35). Chop the dried figs and cook with the water in a small saucepan over a low heat until the water is absorbed and a paste is formed. If it does not seem smooth enough, work in a blender. Leave until cool, then mix with the mashed pumpkin and lemon juice.

Roll out the pastry thinly enough to make 2 × 25 cm (10 inch) circles. Place one in a 25 cm (10 inch) diameter pie dish. Put in the filling but keep a 2.5 cm (1 inch) margin round the outer edge. Place the second circle on top and firmly seal the edges together. A secure way to do this is to press them lightly together and then roll them once inwards so that you have made a rim going all round the tart.

Any leftover pastry can be cut into thin strips and placed across the pastry lid. Cook in a preheated oven (gas 5/375°F/190°C) for 20 minutes, or until well browned.

Makes 14 slices. Each slice is 10 g CHO. 70 kcals.

Tropical Pie

This recipe makes a very light pie.

1 quantity cottage cheese pastry
  (p. 60)

175 g (6 oz) fresh pineapple
  (remove outer skin before
  weighing)

2 medium eating apples,
  weighing 225 g (8 oz)
100 g (4 oz) papaya (paw-paw)
  (if unobtainable substitute
  10 g CHO of another
  tropical fruit, eg 50 g [2 oz]
  fresh dates)

Roll out the pastry thinly enough to make 2 × 25 cm (10 inch) circles. Place one in a 25 cm (10 inch) diameter pie dish. Grate the apples and spread them over the base of the pastry. Chop the pineapple into small chunks and scatter evenly over the apples. Do the same with the papaya. Put on the pastry lid. Mark off into 16 portions.

Bake in a preheated oven (gas 5/375°F/190°C) for 30 minutes until brown and the sides of the pie look crispy.

Makes 16 small portions. Each portion is 10 CHO. 65 kcals.

Nut Pastry

This pastry has a cakey texture.

125 g (4½ oz) wholewheat flour
25 g (1 oz) bran
1 tsp bicarbonate of soda
25 g (1 oz) margarine
25 g (1 oz) ground almonds

25 g (1 oz) unsweetened
   chestnut purée (see p. 41)
2 tsp lemon juice
½ lightly beaten egg*, size 3
75–90 ml (3 fl oz) low-fat
   natural yogurt

Mix the flour, bran and bicarbonate of soda. Rub in the margarine. Add ground almonds and chestnut purée. Mix the chestnut purée well into the flour mixture because it can tend to stick in one lump. Add the lemon juice, half a lightly beaten egg and the yogurt to make a soft dough.

Chill in the fridge for 30 minutes before using.

Total pastry is 100 g CHO. 885 kcals.

German Apple Cake

This is an adaptation of an apple cake for which my friend Erna Weiss is known far and wide. While her tiny seventeenth-century Hampstead house was being renovated, she was forced to spend a lot of her time in a café round the corner where her famous apple cake is now served commercially.

*It can be rather wasteful using half an egg, and as this mixture freezes well, you could simply make double the quantity and put half the pastry in the freezer or use it with one of the recipes based on nut pastry.

1 quantity nut pastry (above)

5 medium eating apples,
   peeled, weighing 650 g (1 lb
   7 oz)

25 ml (1 fl oz) unsweetened
   apple juice.

Roll out the pastry thinly enough to make a top and base for use in a 20 cm (8 inch) square tin. Place one piece of pastry in the tin and press with your fingers around the sides so that the pastry is firmly against the tin. Put some dried beans over the centre to keep the pastry flat while cooking. Cook for 10 minutes in a preheated oven (gas 5/375°F/190°C).

Prepare the filling: cut the cored apples into chunks, about 8–10 per apple. Place the apples into a pan with the apple juice and cook over a low heat for a few minutes until the apples are slightly softened but not mushy. It is important for the texture of the cake that they are quite firm.

Take the pastry out of the oven and pour the apple filling evenly over the base. Use the remaining piece of pastry as the lid. Bake for about 20–25 minutes at the same heat until evenly browned on top.

TOPPING

This topping is what makes the cake so special. Use the recipe for carob fudge icing (p. 112) but instead of 50 ml (2 fl oz) skimmed milk use 100 ml (4 fl oz). This makes a finer topping that is easier to spread thinly.

Makes 20 small iced slices. Each slice is 10 g CHO. 70 kcals.

Meringue Surprises

These are rather elegant biscuits, with shades of a Viennese patisserie about them. They are, in fact, very simple to make.

½ quantity nut pastry (p. 62)

25 g (1 oz) sugar-free strawberry
   jam

1 egg white
50 g (2 oz) dried apricots,
   finely chopped
25 g (1 oz) almond flakes

Roll the pastry out to fit into a 20 cm (8 inch) square tin. Place in tin and bake in a preheated oven (gas 5/375°F/190°C) for 10 minutes.

Spread the jam all over the pastry. Whisk the egg white until stiff and very lightly fold in the chopped apricots and almonds. Spread this mixture on top of the pastry and jam. Return to the oven, reducing the temperature to gas 1/275°F/140°C for 30 minutes or until the meringue is set and lightly browned.

Cut into 16 squares when cold.

Makes 16 squares. 2 squares are 10 g CHO. 90 kcals.

Fig Rolls

1 quantity nut pastry (p. 62)

½ tsp ground ginger
1 tsp cinnamon

100 g (4 oz) dried figs, chopped
50 g (2 oz) prunes, stoned and
   chopped
100 ml (4 fl oz) water

25 ml (1 fl oz) unsweetened
   orange juice
25 g (1 oz) ground walnuts

Simmer the chopped figs and prunes with the water until they form a mushy paste. Blend if necessary. Add the spices. Take off the heat and leave to cool. When cooled, add the orange juice and walnuts.

Roll the pastry into a long oblong shape about 36 × 30.5 cm (14 × 12 inches). Cut it in half lengthways with a sharp knife. Use half the fig filling for each piece of pastry. Spoon the filling into a long thin strip about 30.5 cm (12 inches) along the pastry. Roll the pastry up. The fig filling will probably be covered a couple of times. Mark each roll of pastry into 8 divisions, indicating the slices.

Place on a baking sheet and bake in a preheated oven (gas 4/ 350°F/180°C) for 25 minutes until the pastry is evenly browned.

When it has cooled cut into 16 rolls. Slicing it after baking avoids the filling drying out during the cooking time.

Makes 16 biscuits. Each biscuit is 10 g CHO. 80 kcals.

Many-Layered Tart

Esther and I used to work in the same sculpture workshop together, and over tea breaks she would dispense recipes as other people retail bits of gossip. Years of experience and three children stood behind her cake expertise. Her measurements are 'handfuls' and 'pinches', not quite the accuracy of gram measurement that I have had to get used to, but they adapt quite well.

1 quantity nut pastry (p. 62)

25 g (1 oz) sugar-free apricot jam
40 g (1½ oz) raisins soaked in 25 ml (1 fl oz) water for 15 minutes
1 large eating apple, weighing 150 g (5 oz), thinly sliced

1½ tsp cinnamon
25 g (1 oz) walnuts, finely chopped
15 g (½ oz) unsweetened desiccated coconut
15 g (½ oz) sesame seeds

Roll out the pastry thinly and cut into 4 circles each 18 cm (7 inches) in diameter. Spread 3 circles with some of the apricot jam. Spread the jam more thinly on the fourth circle which will be used as a lid.

Boil up the raisins with the water they have been soaking in, so that they absorb all the water. Leave to cool.

Lay the first circle in an 18 cm (7 inch) diameter baking tin. Cover evenly with the apple. Sprinkle ½ teaspoon of cinnamon over the top. Place next circle on top. Cover with the finely chopped walnuts and sprinkle over ½ teaspoon cinnamon. Place the next circle on top and cover with the raisins. Mix the coconut and ½ teaspoon cinnamon and spoon this over the raisins. Try and keep the fruit as evenly distributed as possible. Place the fourth and final circle on top and sprinkle with sesame seeds, which will stick to the jam.

Bake in a preheated oven (gas 5/375°F/190°C) for 30–35 minutes until nicely browned and crisp on top.

Serve cold.

Makes 8 slices. Each slice is 20 g CHO. 175 kcals.

Carob Kisses

These biscuits are very good for parties with carob fudge filling oozing out of the middle and little dollops sitting on the top.

1 quantity nut pastry (p. 62)

2 quantities carob fudge icing (p. 112)
50 g (2 oz) banana

Roll out the pastry fairly thinly so that you can cut 32 × 5 cm

(2 inch) circles. An oblong about 20 × 46 cm (8 × 16 inches) should be large enough.

Put the circles on a baking sheet and bake in a preheated oven (gas 5/375°F/190°C) for 15 minutes until lightly browned. Leave until cool.

When they have cooled put half a teaspoon of carob fudge icing on each of 16 of the biscuits. Cover with the remaining biscuits. Decorate the top of these with the rest of the icing and a sliver of banana.

Makes 16 biscuits. Each biscuit is 10 g CHO. 95 kcals.

Yeast Pastry

Yeast sounds daunting but this recipe is a boon for the faint-hearted. My sister-in-law, who was staying with us, managed to demonstrate this recipe while I was making breakfast and drawing up insulin, and she was preparing to assault the summer sales. The dough rose while we were otherwise occupied, and the cake was quickly made. The yeast bulks up the flour and makes quite a filling dough for a comparatively low carbohydrate value.

A lot of the yeast pastry recipes use only half the dough, but it is worth making the whole mixture and either baking double the amount and freezing it or using the remaining dough as a base for pizza.

25 ml (1 fl oz) unsweetened orange juice
75 ml (3 fl oz) boiling water
7 g (¼ oz) (or 1 dessertspoon) dried yeast
40 g (1½ oz) margarine

25 ml (1 fl oz) skimmed milk
150 g (5½ oz) wholewheat flour
25 g (1 oz) bran
25 g (1 oz) wheat germ
½ well-beaten egg, size 3

Combine the orange juice and 25 ml (1 fl oz) of the boiling water and wait a minute or so until it becomes lukewarm. Add the yeast and leave for 30 minutes until all the dried granules of yeast have been converted to a liquid form.

Meanwhile prepare a large bowl as you will need to leave room for the dough to rise. Cut up the margarine in the bowl. Pour the rest of the boiling water over the margarine to help it melt. Add the milk and when these liquids are lukewarm add the yeast mixture, 125 g (4½ oz) flour, bran and wheat germ. Fold in the beaten egg.

Either work the mixture in a food processor or mixer or beat with a spoon for about 5 minutes. The dough will become warm and quite sticky. Cover with cling film and a cloth and leave for about an hour until doubled in bulk. (It is possible to make this pastry without beating the dough, but it will then take about 2–2½ hours to rise.)

After it has risen add the remaining flour to make it into a workable dough. This pastry can be rolled out quite thinly on a lightly floured board. It has a stretchy springy feel to it. At a certain point it will go into holes when rolled out, which means you should not roll it any thinner.

With this pastry it is often a good idea to transfer the rolled-out pastry to an ungreased baking tray and fill it on the sheet.

Total yeast pastry is 120 g CHO. 960 kcals.

Apple Yeast Roll

Normal eating apples make up the bulk of the filling for apple yeast roll. Since they are sweet enough to be eaten, the apples do not need to be sprinkled with sugar or honey; only sour 'cooking apples' need sugar. By using an apple that is naturally sweet you can bake your favourite recipe without sugar.

½ quantity yeast pastry (p. 66)   25 g (1 oz) wheat germ
2 tsp cinnamon
25 g (1 oz) sugar-free apricot jam   3 medium eating apples,
25 g (1 oz) ground almonds   weighing 450 g (1 lb), grated

Roll the pastry out into a thin oblong. Spread the surface with jam, leaving a margin of 1 cm (½ inch) around the edges. Cover thinly with the ground almonds and wheat germ mixed with the cinnamon. Sprinkle the grated apples all over this. Roll up swiss-roll fashion and seal the ends of the roll. Leave to rise for 15 minutes.

Transfer to a baking sheet. Bake in a preheated oven (gas 5/375°F/190°C) for 10 minutes and then turn it down to gas 4/350°F/180°C for a further 20–25 minutes until nicely browned.

Makes 12 slices. Each slice is 10 g CHO. 80 kcals.

Carob Ring

½ quantity yeast pastry (p. 66)

25 g (1 oz) sugar-free apricot jam
50 g (2 oz) ground almonds

25 g (1 oz) carob powder
50 g (2 oz) dried figs, chopped
½ orange

Roll the pastry out into a thin oblong, roughly 28 × 20 cm (11 × 8 inches). Spread the surface with the jam, leaving a margin of 1 cm (½ inch) around the edges.

Mix the ground almonds with the carob and figs and spread over the jam. Peel the orange, chop finely and spread over the ground almond mixture. Roll up firmly and seal the ends.

Place the long roll around the central funnel of a greased angel cake tin. It will probably take a little easing to get it into place. Try and ensure that the top is mostly pastry and not filling, because any exposed filling would just become dry during baking. Leave to rise for 20 minutes.

Brush the top with skimmed milk, then bake in a preheated oven (gas 4/350°F/180°C) for 30–40 minutes until browned on top.

Decorate with coconut cream icing (p. 114) when cool.

Makes 10 iced slices. Each slice is 10 g CHO. 125 kcals.

Cinnamon Ring

This recipe is similar to the carob ring. It uses yeast pastry and has an aromatic cinnamon filling combined with soft chewy figs. It also helps to get you familiar with the taste of wheat germ. Once you get used to the taste, try sprinkling a little over your breakfast cereal and stewed fruit. It is rich in vitamin E and the B vitamins.

½ quantity yeast pastry (p. 66)

75 g (3 oz) dried figs (soaked in 75 ml [3 fl oz] water for 15 minutes if quite soft and moist. If they are really dried and hard, leave them soaking in water overnight)

25 g (1 oz) ground almonds
25 g (1 oz) wheat germ
4–5 tsp cinnamon
25 ml (1 fl oz) skimmed milk
25 g (1 oz) sugar-free strawberry jam

Boil the figs in their soaking water so that it is all absorbed. Mix the ground almonds, wheat germ and cinnamon. Pour in the milk which will make the mixture go into thick moist crumbs.

Roll out the pastry as for carob ring, p. 68. Spread the surface with the jam. Cover with the cinnamon mixture. Slice the figs thinly and lay them in a couple of lines across the middle of the pastry. Roll up as for carob ring and place in a lightly greased angel cake tin. Leave to rise, then finish and bake as for carob ring.

Cinnamon ring also looks very good with a thin layer of coconut cream icing (p. 114) on top.

Makes 12 slices. Each slice is 10 g CHO. 85 kcals.

Poppy Seed Yeast Roll

½ quantity yeast pastry (p. 66)   poppy seed filling (see p. 56)

25 g (1 oz) sugar-free apricot jam

Roll the pastry out into a thin oblong. Spread with apricot jam then spread over the filling. Roll up firmly and seal at the ends. Mark off 14 divisions.

Place on a baking sheet and bake in a preheated oven (gas 5/ 375°F/190°C) for 10 minutes, then reduce heat to gas 4/350°F/180°C and cook for a further 25 minutes.

Makes 14 slices. Each slice is 10 g CHO. 85 kcals.

Velvet Plum Cake

This is a sweet yeast cake which you can make towards autumn when the dark purple plums are in season.

½ quantity yeast pastry (p. 66)   350 g (12 oz) purple plums,
                                     stoned and cut into 1 cm
75 g (3 oz) skimmed milk quark   (½ inch) pieces
½ tsp cinnamon   1 large eating apple,
½ tsp vanilla   weighing 175 g (6 oz),
                                     grated
                                   15 g (½ oz) wheat germ

Mix together the quark, cinnamon and vanilla. In a separate bowl, mix the plums and grated apple.

Roll out the yeast pastry to a thin oblong, but not so thin that this stretchy pastry goes into holes – roughly 28 × 20 cm (11 × 8 inches). Spread the length of the middle section, about 28 × 7.5 cm (11 × 3 inches) with the quark mixture. Sprinkle wheat germ evenly along this. Then cover with the plum and apple mixture, distributing it evenly along the length of the pastry. Fold the two flaps over envelope style and seal each end so that the filling will not run out. This also helps to keep the width of the roll even along its whole length, so that it is easy to divide into equal slices.

Place on a baking sheet and bake in a preheated oven (gas 5/ 375°F/190°C) for 10 minutes, then reduce the heat to gas 4/350°F/180°C and cook for another 20 minutes.

Makes 12 slices. Each slice is 10 g CHO. 75 kcals.

Sweet Pie Crust

This pie crust is milk free and egg free. It is excellent for diabetics because it has a low carbohydrate count. The sunflower seeds used in this recipe can be nibbled after a meal or as a snack; 25 g (1 oz) of sunflower seeds contain one third of the average woman's daily requirement of thiamin (vitamin B1) and 15 per cent of her iron needs.

50 g (2 oz) dried figs
50 ml (2 fl oz) water
25 g (1 oz) sunflower seeds
25 g (1 oz) pumpkin seeds
25 g (1 oz) bran

25 g (1 oz) wheat germ
1 tsp cinnamon (optional)
⅛ tsp ground cloves (optional)
⅛ tsp grated nutmeg (optional)

Chop the figs and put in a pan with the water over a low heat. Cook until all the water is absorbed and then blend. Put aside to cool.

Grind the sunflower and pumpkin seeds to powder. Mix in a bowl together with the bran, wheat germ and spices if using. Bind together with the fig paste. It will form into thick crumbs. Work these into a dough.

Pat the dough around the base of a 23 cm (9 inch) pie plate. Bake blind in a preheated oven (gas 4/350°F/180°C) for 15 minutes. Remove from the oven and pour in your favourite pie filling. Sprinkle with a teaspoon of sesame seeds and return to the oven for a further 15 minutes.

Total pie crust is 50 g CHO. 515 kcals.

Apple and Apricot Pie

1 quantity sweet pie crust (above)	300 g (11 oz) fresh apricots
	50 ml (2 fl oz) unsweetened apple juice
2 good-sized eating apples, weighing 275 g (10 oz), sliced	50 ml (2 fl oz) water

Prepare the pie crust as in the recipe above. Put the sliced apples, stoned and sliced apricots, juice and water in a saucepan and heat gently until softened. Pour over the partly cooked pastry crust and return to the oven, at gas 4/350°F/180°C for a further 5 minutes.

Makes 10 slices. Each slice is 10 g CHO. 75 kcals.

Barley Pastry

Barley flour gives pastry a different texture from wholewheat flour. It has a moister, more cake-like texture with a nutty flavour and is not as light as wheat pastry. Make sure that the barley flour you buy, like the wholewheat flour, is ground from the whole grain.

150 g (5 oz) barley flour (whole grain flour)	50 ml (2 fl oz) oil
	50–75 ml (2–3 fl oz) cold water

Put the flour into a bowl. Pour oil into the flour and mix well to form thick crumbs. Bind with as much water as is necessary to make a soft dough. Do not pour all the water in at one go, but add little by little. This pastry when rolled out is quite crumbly and it is just as quick to use your fingers to pat it into shape in a tin.

Total pastry is 110 g CHO. 975 kcals.

Strawberry Jam and Poppy Seed Tart

1 quantity barley pastry (p. 71)   75 g (3 oz) sugar-free
                                            strawberry jam
                                     25 g (1 oz) poppy seeds

Set aside a heaped tablespoon of the pastry then pat the rest evenly over the base of an oblong tin. Spread with the jam. Take the remaining pastry and make into little balls which you flatten between your fingers to form circles about the size of a 5p piece. Dot these all over the jam. Sprinkle the whole of the tart with the poppy seeds. Bake in a preheated oven (gas 5/375°F/190°C) for 30 minutes until browned at the edges. Cut into 14 squares.

Makes 14 squares. 1 square is 10 g CHO. 85 kcals.

Apricot Slices

These taste quite tart, are moist and easily swallowed. The pastry includes oats as well as flour. Apricots have proportionally the highest fibre content of any dried fruit and provide a concentrated source of vitamin A. The Hunzas, who live in the foothills of the Himalayas, eat apricots fresh in season and dry out, as an important part of their diet – they are famously free of most diseases, although of course their lifestyle is very different from ours.

100 g (4 oz) dried apricots   1 tsp cinnamon
200 ml (7 fl oz) water   ⅛ tsp ground cloves
                                     50 g (2 oz) margarine
Pastry   1 tsp almond essence or
100 g (4 oz) wholewheat flour   extract
100 g (4 oz) porridge oats   1 apple or pear, grated

Put the apricots in a bowl and leave to soak in the water overnight. Blend until a purée is formed. You might find you will need to add more water to keep it creamy – it depends on how dry the apricots were to start with.

   To make the pastry, mix the flour, oats and spices. Rub in the margarine. Add the almond essence and grated fruit. Work together with your hands to make a moist dough (a food processor can be used briefly). Divide it in half and pat one half over the base of a 20 cm (8 inch) square tin, pressing with your finger tips to make it even. Roll out the remaining half so it will fit exactly over the top.

Spread the apricot filling over the pastry base. Place the pastry lid on top. Mark off 16 portions. Bake in a preheated oven (gas 4/350°F/180°C) for 35–40 minutes until well browned on top.

Makes 16 slices. Each slice is 10 g CHO. 70 kcals.

Prune Slices

1 quantity pastry used in apricot slices (p. 72)	100 g (4 oz) stoned prunes, cut into pieces
	50 g (2 oz) tofu
200 ml (7 fl oz) boiling water	1 tbls lemon juice

Pour the boiling water over the cut-up prunes. Leave to stand for at least 4 hours or overnight. Boil the prunes in the soaking water until it is all absorbed. Put prunes in the blender (or food processor) together with the tofu and lemon juice. Blend until it becomes a creamy liquid. Prepare the pastry and tin as in apricot slices, above. Pour the prune mixture over the pastry base. Place the pastry lid on top and mark off 16 portions. Bake in a preheated oven (gas 4/350°F/180°C) for 35–40 minutes until well browned on top.

Makes 16 slices. Each slice is 10 g CHO. 80 kcals.

BISCUITS

Rice Banana Peach Drops

This was a recipe put together for tea with a friend who has coeliac disease. She can only eat flours that are gluten-free; this excludes ordinary wholewheat flour. I was faced with the challenge to make something that would suit her and my resident diabetic. The result was a moist and tasty biscuit.

50 g (2 oz) dried dates
50 ml (2 fl oz) water
150 g (5 oz) brown rice flakes
100 g (4 oz) cottage cheese
225 g (8 oz) peeled bananas,
   mashed

1 medium ripe peach,
   coarsely grated (if not in
   season, use an additional
   50 g [2 oz] bananas)
1 tsp vanilla

Cook the dates with the water in a pan over a low heat until a thick paste forms. Blend to make really smooth. Take off the heat to cool.

Put the rice flakes in a bowl. Remove the lumps from the cottage cheese by using either a mouli or a sieve then add to the rice flakes. Add the finely mashed bananas, the peach and vanilla and mix together. Finally add the date paste.

Using a dessertspoon put 18 drops of the mixture on to a lightly greased baking sheet. Bake in a preheated oven (gas 4/350°F/180°C) for 20 minutes or until lightly browned.

Makes 18 small biscuits. Each one is 10 g CHO. 55 kcals.

Peach Walnut Slices

These are thick chewy biscuits.

50 g (2 oz) raisins, soaked in 25
   ml (1 fl oz) water for 15
   minutes
60 g (2½ oz) wholewheat flour
50 g (2 oz) brown rice flakes
1 tsp bicarbonate of soda

1 tsp cinnamon
25 g (1 oz) margarine
15 g (½ oz) walnuts,
   chopped
1 ripe peach, grated

Boil the raisins in their soaking water until it has all been absorbed. Mix together the flour, rice flakes, bicarbonate of soda and cinnamon. Rub in the margarine. Add the raisins and walnuts. Bind with the grated peach and press into a lightly greased 18 cm (7 inch) diameter tin.

Bake in a preheated oven (gas 4/350°F/180°C) for 20–25 minutes until browned and firm. Cut into 12 slices when cool.

Makes 12 small slices. Each slice is 10 g CHO. 65 kcals.

Apricot and Tofu Biscuits

These biscuits are quite filling. The jam on top makes them look a bit different.

25 g (1 oz) sultanas	25 g (1 oz) margarine
25 ml (1 fl oz) water	50 g (2 oz) dried apricots,
100 g (4 oz) wholewheat flour	chopped finely
50 g (2 oz) porridge oats	25 ml (1 fl oz) unsweetened
½ tsp bicarbonate of soda	orange juice
1 tsp cream of tartar	150 g (5 oz) tofu
1 tsp cinnamon	25 g (1 oz) sugar-free apricot
1 tsp mixed spice	jam

Gently heat the sultanas and water in a pan until the water is absorbed, and then work in a blender to make a smooth paste.

Mix the flour, oats, bicarbonate of soda, cream of tartar and spices. Rub in the margarine to make fine crumbs. Add the sultana purée and the chopped apricots. Pour the orange juice over. Bind with tofu which has been blended or put through a mouli. You cannot just mash it in because the firm tofu will remain in lumps and not act as a binding agent.

To make 16 equal-sized biscuits divide the mixture into half and then half again, so that you have four equal-sized pieces of dough. Make 4 biscuits out of each section. To make the biscuits, roll the pieces of dough into balls. Place them on a lightly greased baking sheet. Press gently in the middle of each ball with the index finger so that they are flattened into a round shape, about 4 cm (1½ inches) diameter with a hollow in the centre.

Bake in a preheated oven (gas 4/350°F/180°C) for 30 minutes until the biscuits are brown all over. Put a drop of the apricot jam in the centre hole while the biscuits are still warm.

Makes 16 biscuits. Each biscuit is 10 g CHO. 60 kcals.

Banana Date Drops

Oats are not used just for steaming hot bowls of porridge but also make delicious light biscuits.

75 g (3 oz) dried dates
50 ml (2 fl oz) water
275 g (9 oz) ripe bananas
25 ml (1 fl oz) oil

½ tsp vanilla
100 g (4 oz) porridge oats
25 g (1 oz) wheat germ
25 g (1 oz) bran

Put the dates and water in a pan over a low heat and cook until the water is absorbed. Work in the blender to make a smooth paste. Leave to cool.

Mash the bananas with a fork to make a fine paste. Combine the cooled date paste, mashed bananas, oil and vanilla. Fold in the oats, wheat germ and bran to make a thick consistency. Drop from a dessertspoon on to an ungreased baking sheet. The mixture makes 18 biscuits. Bake in a preheated oven (gas 5/375°F/190°C) for 20 minutes until browned outside.

Makes 18 small drops. 1 drop is 10 g CHO. 65 kcals.

Carob Brownies

These are chewy and scrumptious like all brownies should be. This recipe is best eaten fresh – but let it cool first!

75 g (3 oz) dried dates
50 ml (2 fl oz) water
50 g (2 oz) walnuts
75 g (3 oz) wholewheat flour
25 g (1 oz) carob powder

½ tsp bicarbonate of soda
1 tsp cream of tartar
25 ml (1 fl oz) oil
1 egg, size 3, well beaten
1 tsp vanilla

Put the dates in a pan with the water and cook over a low heat until all the water is absorbed. Blend to make a really smooth paste and leave until cool. Set aside 3 walnuts then grind the rest.

Combine the flour, carob powder, bicarbonate of soda and cream of tartar. Add the oil, date paste, beaten egg and ground walnuts. Pour into a 16 cm (6 inch) diameter greased tin. Grate the reserved walnuts and sprinkle over the top.

Bake in a preheated oven (gas 4/350°F/180°C) for 30–35 minutes until it is springy when you press down the top and a knife inserted into the centre comes out cleanly. Cut into 12 squares when cool.

Makes 12 squares. Each square is 10 g CHO. 85 kcals.

Creamy Carob Squares

100 g (4 oz) dried dates
50 ml (2 fl oz) water
100 g (4 oz) skimmed milk
    quark
15 g ($\frac{1}{2}$ oz) carob powder
50 g (2 oz) walnuts, chopped,
    plus 3 extra walnuts

$\frac{1}{2}$ size 3 well-beaten egg
50 g (2 oz) wholewheat flour
1 tsp vanilla

Gently heat the dates and water in a saucepan until the water is absorbed and a paste formed. Blend to make a really fine paste. Leave until cool.

Combine the quark and carob. Add the cooled date mixture and the chopped walnuts, followed by the egg. Gently stir in the flour and vanilla. Pour into a lightly greased and floured 20 cm (8 inch) square tin. Grate the 3 walnuts over the top of the mixture in the tin.

Bake in a preheated oven (gas 4/350°F/180°C) for 30 minutes until firm and lightly browned on top. Cut into 12 squares for serving.

Makes 12 squares. Each square is 10 g CHO. 70 kcals.

Peanut Biscuits

These are soft and munchy.

150 g (5 oz) dried dates
100 ml (4 fl oz) water
150 g (5 oz) wholewheat flour
½ tsp bicarbonate of soda
1 tsp cream of tartar
150 g (5 oz) smooth peanut
  butter (salt-free and
  sugar-free)

25 ml (1 fl oz) oil
1 tsp vanilla
1 egg, size 3, beaten
50 ml (2 fl oz) unsweetened
  orange juice
4 or 5 chopped raw peanuts
  for decoration

Put the dates and water in a pan over a low heat. Cook until all
the water is absorbed and the dates have become a paste. If it is
still lumpy, blend before using. Leave until cool.

Mix the flour with the bicarbonate of soda and cream of tartar.
Add the peanut butter, date paste, oil and vanilla. Bind with
beaten egg and orange juice. This makes a stiff but moist mixture.

Put a few drops of water on your hands to dampen them and
roll the mixture into 20 balls. To get the balls all more or less the
same size, divide the mixture into quarters and make 5 balls out
of each quarter. Place on a lightly greased baking sheet. Decorate
the top of each ball with a piece of chopped peanut, pressing the
ball down into a round shape on the baking sheet. Bake in a
preheated oven (gas 5/375°F/190°C) for 10–15 minutes.

Makes 20 biscuits. Each biscuit is 10 g CHO. 105 kcals.

Sesame Biscuits

Children love these sweet and chewy biscuits.

100 g (4 oz) dried dates
25 g (1 oz) stoned prunes,
  chopped
100 ml (4 fl oz) water
100 g (4 oz) wholewheat flour

½ tsp bicarbonate of soda
25 ml (1 fl oz) oil
1 egg, size 3, lightly beaten
100 g (4 oz) sesame seeds

Gently heat the dates, prunes and water until they form a thick paste. Blend to make it smooth, then leave until cool.

Mix the flour and bicarbonate of soda, then add the oil and egg. Add the date-prune paste, then mix in the sesame seeds, stirring well.

Put in an oiled 20 cm (8 inch) square tin. Bake in a preheated oven (gas 3/325°F/170°C) for 25 minutes until the mixture in the baking tin has become firm and brown. Cut into 16 squares to serve.

Makes 16 squares. Each square is 10 g CHO. 95 kcals.

Tahini Biscuits

75 g (3 oz) dried dates	100 g (4 oz) wholewheat flour
50 ml (2 fl oz) water	1 tsp cinnamon
100 g (4 oz) tahini	50 ml (2 fl oz) unsweetened
50 g (2 oz) porridge oats	orange juice

Gently heat the dates and water in a small pan. Mash the dates with the back of a spoon until all the water is absorbed and a thick paste is formed. Work in a blender to make really smooth. Allow this mixture to cool for a few minutes.

Combine the date paste with the tahini and fold in the oats, flour and cinnamon. This will make a crumbly dough that will not quite bind. Add the orange juice to make the dough moister. Press with your fingers evenly into a 20 cm (8 inch) square greased tin. Lightly mark off 16 sections with a knife.

Bake in a preheated oven (gas 3/325°F/170°C) for 20–25 minutes until the sides are browned and it is lightly browned on top.

Makes 16 biscuits. Each biscuit is 10 g CHO. 80 kcals.

Cardamom Circles

Cardamom is a very fragrant, exotic-smelling spice. It wafts around the kitchen while these biscuits are in the oven – a tantalizing aroma to anyone passing by.

50 g (2 oz) dried dates
25 g (1 oz) sultanas
50 ml (2 fl oz) water (or, even more fragrant, 25 ml [1 fl oz] rose water and 25 ml [1 fl oz] water)
100 g (4 oz) wholewheat flour

25 g (1 oz) soya flour
25 g (1 oz) ground almonds
1 tsp ground cardamom
½ tsp cinnamon
25 ml (1 fl oz) oil
1 egg, size 3

Cook the dates and sultanas in the water until it has all been absorbed and the dates are reduced to a paste. Leave until cool.

Mix the flours, ground almonds, cardamom and cinnamon. Add the oil and the cooled date-sultana paste. Whisk the egg and use to bind the ingredients. This makes quite a crumbly mixture. Working with your hands, bring it together to form a light pastry. Roll out to just under 1 cm (⅜ inch) thickness, about 28 × 10 cm (11 × 4 inches). You will need hardly any flour to roll this pastry out with. Use a 6 cm (2½ inch) circular cutter to make 12 thick biscuits.

Place on a baking sheet and bake in a preheated oven (gas 3/ 325°F/170°C) for 20 minutes until the biscuits are evenly browned. These biscuits are best eaten the same day.

Makes 12 biscuits. Each biscuit is 10 g CHO. 85 kcals.

Poppy Seed Biscuits

Poppy seeds are a good source of thiamin (part of the B vitamin complex), although you would have to eat about 100 g (4 oz) to reach the recommended daily intake.

60 g (2½ oz) dried figs, chopped
50 ml (2 fl oz) water
100 g (4 oz) wholewheat flour
25 g (1 oz) low-fat soya flour

25 g (1 oz) margarine
50 g (2 oz) poppy seeds, ground
1 tsp rum essence or rum
50 g (2 oz) cottage cheese

Put the figs and water in a pan over a low heat and cook until the water is absorbed. Blend to make a smooth paste and leave until cool.

Mix the flours together. Rub in the margarine. Add the fig paste, ground poppy seeds and rum. To bind with the cottage cheese you need to remove the lumps, so use a blender, mouli or sieve for this purpose. Bind into a soft dough.

Roll the pastry out thinly. Cut with a 7.5 cm (3 inch) diameter cutter to make 22 biscuits. Bake on an ungreased baking sheet in a preheated oven (gas 5/375°F/190°C) for 10–15 minutes until lightly browned.

Makes 22 thin biscuits. 2 biscuits are 10 CHO. 95 kcals.

Prune and Oat Biscuits

These are chunky chewy biscuits that are quite filling.

25 g (1 oz) low-fat soya flour   ½ tsp ground ginger
75 g (3 oz) wholewheat flour   25 ml (1 fl oz) oil
50 g (2 oz) porridge oats   100 g (4 oz) stoned prunes
1 tsp cinnamon   150 ml (5 fl oz) natural low-fat
½ tsp mixed spice   yogurt

Mix the flours, oats and spices, then stir in the oil.

Either grate the prunes finely or chop them finely in a food processor. They break down into very small pieces. Add to the flour mixture and bind with yogurt. Mix thoroughly so that ground prunes are spread evenly throughout the dough.

Roll or pat out to 0.5 cm (¼ inch) thickness, then cut into 14 circles. Place on a baking sheet and bake in a preheated oven (gas 5/375°F/190°C) for 20 minutes until brown on top. Store in a tin.

Makes 14 large biscuits. Each biscuit is 10 g CHO. 70 kcals.

Ginger Biscuits

Oats and rye flour combine to make these moist biscuits.

60 g (2½ oz) dried figs, chopped	½ tsp bicarbonate of soda
50 ml (2 fl oz) water	1 tsp cream of tartar
25 g (1 oz) sultanas	1 tsp ground ginger
25 ml (1 fl oz) oil	½ tsp cinnamon
50 g (2 oz) porridge oats	pinch of grated nutmeg
75 g (3 oz) rye flour (ground	pinch of ground cloves
from the whole grain)	100 ml (4 fl oz) skimmed milk
25 g (1 oz) wheat germ	

Put the figs and water in a small pan and cook over a low heat until the water is absorbed. Work in a blender to make a smooth paste. Leave until cool.

Mix together the cooled fig paste, the sultanas and the oil. Combine the oats, flour, wheat germ, bicarbonate of soda, cream of tartar and the spices. Add the fig mixture, then pour in the milk to give a sticky consistency.

Pour into a lightly greased 20 cm (8 inch) square tin. Bake in a preheated oven (gas 4/350°F/180°C) for 20 minutes until browned and firm. Cut into 16 squares when cooled.

Makes 16 small biscuits. 1 biscuit is 10 g CHO. 60 kcals.

SCONES, MUFFINS AND TEACAKES

SCONES

Scones are a welcome treat for tea. For the best results a few points are worth remembering:

- As you rub in the margarine handle the mixture as little as possible so that it does not become overworked.
- When rolling out use as light a touch as possible. Do not over-roll. If you have any leftover pastry after the first rolling lightly pat it into rounds and then cut, rather than rerolling.
- Make sure the oven is preheated because scones are cooked at a very high temperature for a short period of time. If they have to stay too long in the oven because it was not hot enough they can lose their softness.
- You do not need to grease the baking tray when making scones.
- Scones can be prepared beforehand and stored in the fridge for a few hours before baking.
- Scones freeze well (see p. 19).

Plain Scones

The carrot juice in this sweetens the scones subtly.

150 g (5 oz) wholewheat flour
50 g (2 oz) oat bran and oat germ
½ tsp bicarbonate of soda
1 tsp cream of tartar
25 g (1 oz) margarine

75 ml (3 fl oz) carrot juice or
   unsweetened orange juice
25–40 ml (1–1½ fl oz)
   skimmed milk

Mix the flour, oat bran and germ, bicarbonate of soda and cream of tartar together. Rub in the margarine. Bind with the juice and enough milk to make a soft dough. Roll out to just under 1 cm (⅜ inch) thickness and cut into 12 circles, 6 cm (2½ inches) in diameter. Put on an ungreased baking sheet and bake in a very hot preheated oven (gas 8/450°F/230°C) for about 10 minutes until evenly browned.

Makes 12 scones. Each scone is 10 g CHO. 75 kcals.

Carob Scones

Follow the recipe for plain scones above but use 125 g (4½ oz) wholewheat flour and 25 g (1 oz) carob powder.

Makes 12 scones. Each scone is 10 g CHO. 75 kcals.

Marmalade Scones

150 g (5 oz) wholewheat flour	25 g (1 oz) margarine
50 g (2 oz) bran	50 g (2 oz) sugar-free
½ tsp bicarbonate of soda	marmalade
1 tsp cream of tartar	2 tsp finely grated orange rind
	50 ml (2 fl oz) skimmed milk

Mix the flour, bran, bicarbonate of soda and cream of tartar together. Rub in the margarine. Stir in the marmalade and grated orange rind, making sure they are spread evenly through the flour mixture. Bind to a soft dough with the milk.

Roll out to 0.5–1 cm (¼–⅜ inch) thickness and cut into 6 cm (2½ inch) circles. This mixture makes 12 good-sized scones. Put on to an ungreased baking sheet. Bake in a very hot oven (gas 8/ 450°F/ 230°C) for about 10 minutes until evenly browned. Serve plain or with a sugar-free jam or carob spread.

Makes 12 scones. Each scone is 10 g CHO. 70 kcals.

Pumpkin Scones

These are very light. Pumpkin is another vegetable that is naturally sweet.

225 g (8 oz) wholewheat flour	2 tsp grated lemon rind
25 g (1 oz) bran	225 g (8 oz) mashed cooked
½ tsp bicarbonate of soda	pumpkin (for instructions
1 tsp cream of tartar	on cooking pumpkin see
50 g (2 oz) margarine	p. 35)

Mix the flour, bran, bicarbonate of soda and cream of tartar. Rub in the margarine and add the grated lemon rind. Bind with mashed pumpkin, but make sure you drain off any liquid that might have gathered while it has been standing in the bowl. This should give a moist light dough.

Roll or pat out to just under 1 cm (⅜ inch) thickness and cut into 16 rounds. Put on to an ungreased baking sheet and bake in a preheated oven (gas 8/450°F/230°C) for 10–15 minutes until lightly browned on top. If you lift them off the sheet they will be browned underneath as well.

Makes 16 scones. Each scone is 10 g CHO. 70 kcals.

Prune Scones

This is the type of scone that will have everyone coming back for more.

150 g (5 oz) wholewheat flour
½ tsp bicarbonate of soda
1 tsp cream of tartar
25 g (1 oz) margarine

50 g (2 oz) mashed potato
75 g (3 oz) carrot, finely
  grated
75 g (3 oz) stoned prunes
40–50 ml (2 fl oz) skimmed
  milk

Mix the flour with the bicarbonate of soda and cream of tartar. Rub in the margarine. Add the mashed potato and grated carrot. Grind the prunes, then mix in well with the rest of the ingredients. Bind with enough of the milk to make a soft dough.

Roll out to about 0.5 cm (¼ inch) thick. Use a 6 cm (2½ inch) cutter to cut out 14 scones. Bake on an ungreased baking sheet in a preheated oven (gas 8/450°F/230°C) for 10 minutes until nicely browned. These taste good served either hot or cold.

Makes 14 scones. Each scone is 10 g CHO. 60 kcals.

Apple Scones

These scones have quite a dense texture, so although they are not as large as ordinary scones, they are quite filling. They have a moist, earthy taste.

50 g (2 oz) brown rice flour   1 tsp cinnamon
50 g (2 oz) wholewheat flour   100 ml (4 fl oz) skimmed milk
25 g (1 oz) bran   1 eating apple, grated
25 g (1 oz) wheat germ

Mix the rice flour, wholewheat flour, bran, wheat germ and cinnamon. Bind with the grated apple and milk to make a soft dough. Divide the dough into 10 pieces and flatten each into a roundish cake. Bake on an ungreased baking sheet in a preheated oven (gas 4/350°F/180°C) for about 15 minutes.

Makes 10 scones. Each scone is 10 g CHO. 55 kcals.

Barley Scones

These taste like a cross between scones and rolls, and because the barley flour gives a moist quality you can bake them the night before to eat at breakfast.

150 g (5 oz) barley flour   ½ tsp bicarbonate of soda
50 g (2 oz) wholewheat flour   25 g (1 oz) margarine
25 g (1 oz) bran   100–125 ml (4–4½ fl oz)
1 tsp cream of tartar   skimmed milk

Mix the flours, bran, cream of tartar and bicarbonate of soda. Rub in the margarine and add enough milk to make a moist mixture. Knead lightly and form into 8 rolls; each roll will weigh about 40 g (1½ oz). Place them on a lightly greased baking sheet and brush the tops of the rolls with milk. Bake them in a preheated hot oven (gas 7–8/425–450°F/220–230°C) for about 15 minutes.

Makes 8 rolls. Each roll is 20 g CHO. 115 kcals.

MUFFINS

Sweet muffins can be eaten hot or cold. They have a more cake-like texture than scones because they include an egg. They are quick to make. Plain ones are made of wheat flour, egg, milk and margarine but muffins also provide an opportunity for mixing flours and flavours.

Plain Muffins

This is a quick and easy recipe.

150 g (5 oz) wholewheat flour
25 g (1 oz) wheat germ
1 tsp cream of tartar
½ tsp bicarbonate of soda
25 ml (1 fl oz) oil

1 egg, size 3, well beaten
50 ml (2 fl oz) unsweetened
  orange juice
100 ml (4 fl oz) skimmed milk

Mix the flour, wheat germ, cream of tartar and bicarbonate of soda. Add the oil, beaten egg, orange juice and milk. This makes a mixture with a moist consistency. Lightly grease 12 deep patty tins and spoon the mixture into them. Bake in a preheated oven (gas 7/425°F/220°C) for 15 minutes until the muffins are browned and firm. They rise considerably during cooking.

Makes 12 muffins. Each muffin is 10 g CHO. 75 kcals.

Apple and Pineapple Muffins

These muffins are made without eggs.

75 g (3 oz) wholewheat flour
50 g (2 oz) porridge oats
25 g (1 oz) bran
1 tsp cream of tartar
½ tsp bicarbonate of soda
1 medium eating apple

90 g (3½ oz) fresh pineapple
  (remove outer skin before
  weighing)
25 ml (1 fl oz) oil
100 g (4 oz) firm tofu
50 ml (2 fl oz) skimmed milk

Mix the flour, oats, bran, cream of tartar and bicarbonate of soda. Grate the apple on a very fine grater so that it becomes quite mushy. Chop the pineapple into small pieces. Stir the apple, pineapple and oil into the flours. Blend the tofu or put it through a mouli then use to bind the mixture. Add the milk to give a moist consistency.

Bake in 12 lightly greased patty tins in a preheated oven (gas 5/ 375°F/190°C) for 30 minutes. Cook until they are browned and a knife inserted in the centres comes out cleanly.

Makes 12 muffins. Each muffin is 10 g CHO. 75 kcals.

Banana Muffins

These muffins are egg free and milk free. I have avoided using milk by substituting soya milk. Soya milk is made from soya beans and water. Some people have difficulty digesting milk and find that it leads to allergic reactions – in these cases soya milk can be substituted for cows' milk in recipes. The amount of vitamins and minerals it contains are often less than in skimmed milk. Soya milk contains half as much calcium as fresh skimmed milk, more fat (although not as much as ordinary milk), a little more iron and a little more vitamin B6. Tofu, which is also used here, has much the same quantity of calcium as milk.

25 g (1 oz) porridge oats	75 g (3 oz) bananas, mashed
50 g (2 oz) bran	100 g (4 oz) firm tofu
75 g (3 oz) wholewheat flour	25 g (1 oz) sultanas, soaked
1 tsp bicarbonate of soda	for 15 minutes before use
2 tsp cream of tartar	200 ml (8 fl oz) soya milk
25 ml (1 fl oz) oil	

Mix the oats, bran, flour, bicarbonate of soda and cream of tartar. Add the oil and mashed banana. Blend the tofu or put it through a mouli, then add together with the sultanas. Make into a moist consistency with the soya milk. Use lightly greased muffin holders or a deep jam tart tray. (I often heat it in the oven before spooning the mixture in.) Bake in a preheated oven (gas 5/375°F/190°C) for 25–30 minutes until browned on top and firm.

Makes 12 muffins. Each muffin is 10 g CHO. 85 kcals.

Brown Rice Muffins

150 g (5 oz) cooked brown rice (use 50 g [2 oz] raw rice)
75 g (3 oz) wholewheat flour
1 tsp bicarbonate of soda
50 g (2 oz) cottage cheese

15 g ($\frac{1}{2}$ oz) sultanas
1 peach, grated (if out of season use 1 medium eating apple)
$\frac{1}{2}$ tsp cinnamon (optional)
1 egg, size 3

Put the cold cooked rice in a bowl with the flour and bicarbonate of soda. Stir together so that the rice is coated with flour. Either mouli or sieve the cottage cheese so that all the lumps are removed, then add to rice mixture. Mix in sultanas, grated peach and cinnamon, if using. Lightly beat the egg and use to bind. This gives a fairly moist mixture.

Spoon into lightly greased muffin holders or a deep jam tart tray and cook for 20 minutes in a preheated oven (gas 5/375°F/190°C). Serve warm. If you are in a hurry these can be cooked on a lightly greased griddle or in a heavy frying pan.

Makes 10 muffins. Each muffin is 10 g CHO. 65 kcals.

TEACAKES

These all have quite a rich taste and can be eaten either by themselves or with a spread.

Prune Loaf

100 g (4 oz) wholewheat flour
25 g (1 oz) pumpkin seeds, ground
25 g (1 oz) bran
1 tsp cream of tartar
½ tsp bicarbonate of soda
25 ml (1 fl oz) oil

75 g (3 oz) stoned prunes, soaked in 75 ml (3 fl oz) water for 30 minutes
1 medium eating apple, grated
100 ml (4 fl oz) skimmed milk
1 tsp sesame seeds

Combine the flour, ground pumpkin seeds, bran, cream of tartar and bicarbonate of soda. Stir in the oil. Boil the prunes in their soaking water until it is all absorbed. Blend the prunes to a paste and add, together with the grated apple. Bind with the milk. Pour the mixture into a lightly greased and floured loaf tin. Sprinkle the top with a teaspoon of sesame seeds.

Bake in a preheated oven (gas 5/375°F/190°C) for 20 minutes, then reduce heat to gas 4/350°F/180°C for another 15 minutes. The loaf should be brown and firm.

Makes 12 small slices. Each slice is 10 g CHO. 80 kcals.

Apricot Loaf

Substitute 75 g (3 oz) dried apricots for the prunes and proceed as in prune loaf, above.

Makes 12 small slices. Each slice is 10 g CHO. 80 kcals.

Fruit Spice Loaf

This is based on a recipe created by Rachel, the mother of my daughter's best friend. She is one of the moving forces behind this book because while we were still trying to come to terms with diabetes she was already thinking how to adapt her delicious cakes and biscuits so that they would be diabetically suitable, and all the lovely teas we always had together could continue as before.

50 g (2 oz) dried dates
125 ml (5 fl oz) water
40 g (1½ oz) dried figs, chopped
1 tsp bicarbonate of soda
¼ tsp ground cloves
1 tsp ground ginger
½ tsp cinnamon
1 tsp vanilla

50 g (2 oz) rye flour (ground from the whole grain)
50 g (2 oz) bran
25 g (1 oz) pumpkin seeds, ground
100 ml (4 fl oz) soya milk
3–4 brazil nuts, grated

Put the dates and 50 ml (2 fl oz) water in a small saucepan and cook over a low heat until the water is absorbed and forms a mushy paste. If necessary blend to a fine paste. Combine the date paste with the figs, bicarbonate of soda, spices and vanilla. Pour 75 ml (3 fl oz) boiling water over these ingredients and mix them together. Add the flour, bran and ground pumpkin seeds. Mix with the soya milk to give a smooth consistency.

Pour into a lightly greased small loaf tin and sprinkle a few grated brazil nuts over the top. Cook in preheated oven (gas 3/ 325°F/170°C) for 45–55 minutes.

Makes 10 slices. Each slice is 10 g CHO. 70 kcals.

Peanut Butter Teacake

This teabread has an unusual nutty taste.

50 g (2 oz) dried dates
50 ml (2 fl oz) water
100 g (4 oz) wholewheat flour
25 g (1 oz) low-fat soya flour
½ tsp cinnamon
½ tsp mixed spice
½ tsp grated orange rind

1 tsp cream of tartar
½ tsp bicarbonate of soda
25 g (1 oz) smooth peanut butter (sugar-free and salt-free)
100 ml (4 fl oz) skimmed milk
2–3 peanuts, finely grated

Cook the dates and water in a small pan over a low heat until all the water is absorbed. Blend to a smooth paste, then leave to cool.

Mix the flours, spices, orange rind, cream of tartar and bicarbonate of soda. Mix in the peanut butter and date paste. Stir in the milk to give a moist consistency. Spoon into a lightly greased tin about 15–18 cm (6–7 inches) in diameter. Sprinkle the top with finely grated peanuts. Bake in a preheated oven (gas 4/ 350°F/180°C) for 25–30 minutes, until browned and firm.

Makes 10 small slices. Each slice is 10 g CHO. 70 kcals.

GRIDDLE SCONES

Griddle scones or drop scones are traditionally cooked on a griddle instead of in the oven. Cooking on a griddle meant something could be cooked more quickly, and if used outdoors over a fire, more simply than in the oven. A heavy frying pan can be substituted for a griddle. I use a cast-iron one. If you look after it carefully you will only need to use a minimum of oil. Rub over with oil as you would a baking tin. You will find that if you cook more than one batch of scones you will not need to grease the surface the second time round.

After using, wipe the inside of the pan with some kitchen paper and a little salt, rather than washing it up. Soaking a frying pan in water for a length of time makes food more likely to stick and when you use it again you find yourself having to increase the amount of oil. A non-stick pan can be used but if it is not a heavy pan the drop scones will brown too quickly and the heat will not go steadily through to the centre without burning the outside.

Sultana Griddle Scones or Drop Scones

These scones have a very bread-like texture even though they are cooked on a griddle or pan.

150 g (5 oz) wholewheat flour	25 g (1 oz) margarine
50 g (2 oz) bran	25 g (1 oz) sultanas
1 tsp bicarbonate of soda	1 egg, size 3, well beaten
2 tsp cream of tartar	150 ml (5 fl oz) skimmed milk

Mix the flour, bran, bicarbonate of soda and cream of tartar. Rub in the margarine. Sprinkle the sultanas over this mixture. Bind with the beaten egg and milk to give a fairly thick consistency.

Heat the griddle or heavy pan and put a teaspoon or so of oil around the base. Use generous tablespoon measures to make 14 scones. Cook for about 5–8 minutes on each side, making sure they are cooked all the way through.

Makes 14 scones. Each scone is 10 g CHO. 65 kcals.

Pumpkin Seed Drop Scones

These drop scones are very light and provide more than the usual amount of scone per 10 g CHO.

50 g (2 oz) pumpkin seeds, ground	1 egg, size 3, well beaten
50 g (2 oz) bran	100 ml (4 fl oz) skimmed milk
25 g (1 oz) wheat germ	50 ml (2 fl oz) unsweetened orange juice

Mix the ground pumpkin seeds, bran and wheat germ together. Add the beaten egg and bind together with the milk and orange juice.

Cook either in a non-stick pan or a heavy cast-iron pan which is very lightly oiled. Put 12 spoonfuls on to the cooking surface and cook until brown on both sides. Serve hot. They taste good with sweet or savoury spreads.

Makes 12 scones. 3 scones are 10 g CHO. 145 kcals.

Oat Griddle Scones

At different times in this century oats have played a role in diabetic diets. Around 1905 Von Noorden, a Dutch nutritionist, used oats as the basis for a high carbohydrate diet for diabetics. Oats and the high carbohydrate approach lapsed with the advent of insulin but have re-emerged in recent years, with the view that glucose tolerance improves with an increasing proportion of unrefined carbohydrate in the diet.

50 g (2 oz) porridge oats	1 egg, size 3, well beaten
50 g (2 oz) wholewheat flour	(optional)
150 ml (5 fl oz) low-fat natural yogurt	

Combine the oats and flour. Bind with the yogurt and beaten egg if you are using it. These scones work well with or without adding an egg. The egg makes them slightly lighter, but if you need to keep your egg quota down you can leave the egg out in this recipe. Leave to stand for 15 minutes before cooking.

Lightly grease a griddle or heavy pan and heat. Spoon 9 scones on to the griddle and cook until brown on both sides.

Makes 9 scones. Each scone is 10 g CHO. 65 kcals.

Cornmeal Griddle Scones

Try and vary your teatime treats by using other grains than wheat. Corn or maize flour is a deep yellow colour and has its own particular sweet taste. It is a coarser flour than wheat and makes for an interesting texture. These scones are best eaten hot; they tend to be rather dry when cold.

100 g (4 oz) cornmeal (ground from the whole grain)	1 egg, size 3, well beaten
25 g (1 oz) wholewheat flour	150 ml (5 fl oz) low-fat natural yogurt
25 g (1 oz) wheat germ	

Mix the flours and wheat germ. Add the beaten egg and fold in the yogurt to give a moist consistency.

Cook on a very slightly greased griddle or heavy frying pan. Put 11 heaped tablespoons of the mixture on the cooking surface. Brown on both sides.

Makes 11 scones. Each one is 10 g CHO. 70 kcals.

Carob Millet Drop Scones

If you have not yet used any millet in your cooking this recipe is a gentle introduction. You may have thought that only budgerigars ate millet but outside Europe it often serves as the staple diet. It has a sweet bland taste and is gluten free. It is reputed to be easily digested. The carob adds sweetness and fibre – it contains slightly more fibre per 25 g (1 oz) than bran.

100 g (4 oz) millet flakes	1 egg, size 3, well beaten
25 g (1 oz) carob powder	½ tsp vanilla
¼ tsp cinnamon (optional)	50 g (2 oz) banana, peeled and mashed
200 ml (7 fl oz) boiling water	

Mix the millet flakes, carob and cinnamon, if using, in a bowl. Pour the boiling water over and mix into a stiff paste. Leave to cool, then add the beaten egg, vanilla and mashed banana.

Drop 10 spoonfuls of the mixture on to a lightly greased griddle or heavy frying pan. Brown on each side. Serve hot. These scones are firm on the outside with a soft, almost porridge-like texture inside.

Makes 10 small scones. Each scone is 10 g CHO. 50 kcals.

Oat and Seaweed Griddle Cakes

As a change from the familiar sultana scones and fruit loaves this recipe is based on the Welsh recipe for laver bread. Away from Wales and the west coast of Britain it is hard to obtain laver or sea lettuce. The Japanese equivalent, available in some health food shops, is called nori. All seaweeds have something beneficial to contribute to the diet as they are a good source of trace elements. Laver used to be known as a cure for 'the stone in the bladder'. The laver is prepared by washing and boiling for a long time until it becomes a stiff green mush. It is then strained and stored. The seaweed I used in this recipe was kombu which was the most readily available in my local health food shop. It was described on the packet as being suitable for salads and was dried and shredded into fine strips like grass. The first time you make this recipe, start off with a little seaweed and then gradually increase the amount when you repeat it, to avoid too much of a shock from the unusual taste. Seaweed can be used more subtly in soups and stews. It will blend in with all the other flavours and still impart its own goodness.

200 ml (8 fl oz) boiling water   100 g (4 oz) porridge oats
up to 15 g ($\frac{1}{2}$ oz) laver, salad
    kombu or other seaweed

Pour the boiling water over the salad kombu. Work in the blender so that the kombu is reduced to small pieces. Combine with the oats and add more boiling water if necessary to make a soft dough. Divide into 8 rounds. Cook on a lightly greased griddle or heavy pan for 5 or 10 minutes on each side. These griddle cakes have a fresh moist taste.

Makes 8. Each one is 10 g CHO. 50 kcals.

PANCAKES

Pancakes, crêpes, palachintkas, blintzes are different names for more or less the same batter. In some countries more eggs or milk are used (the Viennese add soda water), some pancakes are cooked paper thin, others are thick and hearty.

A few tips for good results:

- Always let the batter stand for at least half an hour before using.
- Heat frying pan well before pouring batter in.
- Spread batter as thinly as possible over the base of the pan.

Pancakes

Wheat germ has its own natural sweetness and this is imparted to the pancakes in this recipe.

75 g (3 oz) wholewheat flour
5 g (1 tbls) wheat germ
1 egg, size 3, well beaten

175–200 ml (6–7 fl oz) skimmed milk

Mix the flour and wheat germ. Make a well in the centre of the flour and pour the well-beaten egg into it, gradually folding in some of the flour to make a thick mixture. Gradually add 150–175 ml (5–6 fl oz) milk to form a smooth, liquid batter. Leave to stand in the fridge for at least 30 minutes. Before using you will find the batter has thickened so add the final 25 ml (1 fl oz) milk.

Use this quantity to make 6 pancakes. Cook one at a time in a hot frying pan until lightly browned on both sides. The pancakes are delicious served sweet and sour with lemon and sugar-free jam.

Makes 6 pancakes. Each pancake is 10 g CHO. 65 kcals.

Banana Fritters

1 quantity pancake batter (above)
200 g (7 oz) peeled, banana

Cut the banana into thin slices and add to the batter after it has stood in the fridge for at least 30 minutes.

Heat the frying pan. Use a little oil to grease the base. Drop spoonfuls of banana and batter into the hot frying pan, the batter will spread out around the banana. The banana makes the pancake batter sweet and gives it a munchy texture.

Makes 5 large portions. Each portion is 20 g CHO. 110 kcals.

Hungarian Pancakes

We used to frequent a small Hungarian restaurant, where senior civil servants would come to intrigue and the waiter was always prepared to offer advice whether the goulash was fresher than the meat balls and dumplings. The one dish whose quality never varied was the dessert – palachintkas served with chocolate sauce and nuts; this is a sugar-free surrogate.

1 quantity pancake batter (p. 97)	50 ml (2 fl oz) unsweetened orange juice
Filling	1 tsp rum or rum essence
25 g (1 oz) carob powder	25 g (1 oz) finely chopped almonds or ground almonds
pinch of cinnamon	
100 ml (4 fl oz) skimmed milk	
	50 g (2 oz) peeled banana, finely chopped

To make the filling, mix the carob, cinnamon and milk in a small pan over a low heat until the carob has dissolved. Add the orange juice and rum. Take off the heat and add the almonds (if serving children under five years old use the ground almonds rather than chopped) and chopped banana.

If you are serving this recipe for a special occasion cook all the pancakes at one go and keep warm in an ovenproof dish covered with foil in a moderate oven. Heat the sauce so that it bubbles, and either spread over individual pancakes or layer them on top of each other like a cake and slice at the table.

Makes 6 pancakes. Each pancake is 15 g CHO. 115 kcals.

SWEETS AND PARTY TREATS

Carob powder really comes into its own with these recipes for sweets and petits fours. Carob, combined with creamy pastes, tastes almost like chocolate, but without any of the side effects (see p. 39). The carob sweet recipes can be made very quickly and are ideal for parties.

Covered with foil or cling film, they can be kept in the fridge for 4–5 days. They also freeze well, but do freeze on the day you make them. Wrap in cling film or foil and put in a freezer bag (see p. 19).

Many of these recipes have a high nut content, either almonds, peanuts or walnuts. This makes them very rich and you will find that you can only eat a few at a time.

Carob Seed Balls

In my search for healthy beneficial food for a diabetic diet I was introduced to Emile Just, who advocates a macrobiotic diet. The basic doctrine of the macrobiotics is that you are what you eat – so if you eat well you feel well and if you eat badly then you feel bad. What is 'good' and 'bad' is something the nutritionists have spent many years arguing over. As an ordinary consumer one has to rely to some extent on instinct and how you feel. It is useful to know about unusual foods that one would not have normally considered eating. One of Emile Just's many suggestions that we found particularly satisfying is pumpkin seeds. He maintains that pumpkin seeds are beneficial for diabetics and they benefit the pancreas. There is not any scientific evidence to support this. Jane Kinderlehrer, in her wholefood cookbook, cites them as 'a good source of zinc'.

25 g (1 oz) dried dates, finely
   chopped
50 ml (2 fl oz) boiled water
50 g (2 oz) pumpkin seeds,
   ground
50 g (2 oz) wheat germ
25 g (1 oz) carob powder

50 g (2 oz) peanut butter
   (sugar-free and salt-free)
50 ml (2 fl oz) unsweetened
   orange juice
a little unsweetened
   desiccated coconut

Pour the boiling water over the chopped dates and mix with a spoon so that all the water is absorbed and a paste-like effect is achieved. Leave until cool.

Combine the ground pumpkin seeds, wheat germ, carob and peanut butter. Add the cooled dates. Bind with the orange juice. Roll the paste into 24 little balls. Roll them all in a plate of coconut so that they are well coated.

Makes 24 balls. 3 balls are 10 g CHO. 120 kcals.

Sesame Seed Crunch

This is very rich tasting. You will probably find that you can only eat a limited amount at one go, but it is very enjoyable as a sweet finish to a meal.

125 g (4½ oz) sesame seeds
75 g (3 oz) dried figs
15 g (½ oz) carob powder
50 ml (2 fl oz) water
15 g (½ oz) porridge oats, ground
   fine

25 g (1 oz) unsweetened
   desiccated coconut
25 g (1 oz) tahini
25 g (1 oz) peanut butter
1 tsp vanilla
25 ml (1 fl oz) unsweetened
   orange juice

Toast the sesame seeds slowly under the grill. Shake around so that the ones which are underneath also get toasted.

In a small pan heat the chopped figs, carob powder and water until a sauce forms. Take off the heat and add the ground oats, coconut, tahini and peanut butter. Add the vanilla and orange juice. Press into a greased 15 cm (6 inch) tin and chill in the fridge for a couple of hours before serving.

Makes 10 slices. Each slice is 10 g CHO. 145 kcals.

Carob Crunch

Popular with children and adults alike.

50 g (2 oz) flaked almonds   30 ml (2 tbls) water
50 g (2 oz) sultanas $\frac{1}{4}$ tsp vanilla
15 g ($\frac{1}{2}$ oz) carob powder

Chop the almond flakes into halves. Wash, drain and chop sultanas into quarters. Put the carob, water and vanilla in a small pan and heat gently until the carob powder has dissolved. Add the sultanas and almond flakes to the carob mixture. While stirring it does not matter if the almond flakes get further crushed. When the sultanas and almond flakes are well coated put them in a small tin. Leave to chill in the fridge for 2 hours.

An alternative method of serving is to put teaspoonfuls of the mixture into little paper cases.

Makes 4 slices. Each slice is 10 g CHO. 110 kcals.

Carob Chew

This has a very fudgy texture.

50 g (2 oz) raisins, chopped and   25 g (1 oz) carob powder
   soaked in 25 ml (1 fl oz)   50 g (2 oz) sesame seeds
   water for 15 minutes   25 g (1 oz) sugar-free apricot
100 g (4 oz) smooth peanut   jam
   butter (sugar-free and
   salt-free)

Boil the raisins in their soaking water until all the water is absorbed. Mix the peanut butter, carob powder, sesame seeds and raisins. This makes quite a dry mixture, but by adding the apricot jam it becomes moist. Press into an 18 cm (7 inch) diameter tin. Leave in the fridge for 2 hours to chill. Cut into slices and serve.

Makes 8 slices. Each slice is 10 g CHO. 140 kcals.

Carob Halva

This is a quick recipe to make and the results are good. This recipe is quite high in carbohydrate content but you will find that this is something you nibble at after a meal rather than eat in huge quantities.

100 g (4 oz) sultanas	25 g (1 oz) carob powder
75 g (3 oz) tahini	½ tsp cinnamon

Wash, drain and dry the sultanas and blend until they are reduced to a paste. Add the tahini, carob and cinnamon to form a soft dough. Pat into an oblong shape. Cover with foil and chill in the fridge for a couple of hours before serving.

Makes 8 small slices. Each slice is 10 g CHO. 90 kcals.

Carob Fig Balls

These require very little cooking. They are soft and creamy and literally melt in your mouth.

100 g (4 oz) dried figs	15 g (½ oz) ground oats
50 ml (2 fl oz) water	15 g (½ oz) ground almonds
25 g (1 oz) carob powder	15 g (½ oz) walnuts, chopped
50 ml (2 fl oz) skimmed milk	1 tsp rum essence or rum

Heat the chopped figs and water until all the water has been absorbed. Blend to make a smooth paste. In a small pan gently heat the margarine, carob and milk until the carob dissolves to make a dark paste. Leave until cool.

Add the ground oats, ground almonds, chopped walnuts and rum to the carob mixture. Bind with the fig paste. Roll the mixture into 16 small balls, moistening your hands with cold water to stop the mixture sticking. Chill in the fridge for a couple of hours before serving.

Makes 16 balls. 2 balls are 10 g CHO. 60 kcals.

Apricot and Apple Balls

A delicate petit four, with a fresh pleasant flavour.

75 g (3 oz) dried apricots, soaked
   in 75 ml (3 fl oz) water for 30
   minutes
50 g (2 oz) ground almonds
25 g (1 oz) wheat germ

$\frac{1}{8}$ tsp ground cloves
$\frac{1}{8}$ tsp cinnamon
1 medium eating apple, finely
   grated
1 egg white, stiffly beaten

Boil the apricots in their soaking water until it is all absorbed. Leave until cool, then blend into a paste.

Add the ground almonds, wheat germ, spices and apple. Bind the mixture with the stiffly beaten egg white. Using a teaspoon drop spoonfuls of the mixture on to a lightly greased baking sheet to make 20 balls.

Bake in a preheated oven (gas 3/325°F/170°C) for 12–15 minutes until lightly browned, firm on the outside and soft inside. Store in a cool place.

Makes 20 balls. 4 balls are 10 g CHO. 110 kcals.

Apricot Balls

These are very exotic-tasting. The aromatic cardamom spice mixed with the toasted sesame seed produces a delightful blend of flavours.

25 g (1 oz) sesame seeds
100 g (4 oz) dried apricots

25 g (1 oz) chopped almonds
$\frac{1}{2}$ tsp ground cardamom

Toast the sesame seeds under the grill and leave to cool. Chop the apricots finely and mix with the chopped nuts and cardamom. Divide the mixture into 20 small balls. Put the cooled sesame seeds on a small plate and roll the apricot balls in the seeds until they are well coated.

Makes 20 balls. 4 balls are 10g CHO. 95 kcals.

Cinnamon Balls

The strong cinnamon flavour gives these a mellow taste. They are hard to resist. Serve as sweets or after-dinner petits fours.

100 g (4 oz) dried dates
2–3 tsp cinnamon
100 ml (4 fl oz) water
100 g (4 oz) ground almonds

50 g (2 oz) porridge oats,
  ground fine
1 egg white, beaten stiff

Heat the chopped dates, cinnamon and water in a small pan until all the water is absorbed and a paste is formed. Blend to a smooth consistency. Leave until cool.

Pour the date mixture into a bowl and add the ground almonds and ground oats. Bind with a stiffly beaten egg white. Roll into 20 small balls (moisten your hands with cold water to stop the mixture sticking) and place on a lightly greased baking sheet. Bake in a preheated oven (gas 3/325°F/170°C) for 15 minutes, so that they are slightly brown on the outside and underneath. They should be firm on the outside but with a soft cakey texture inside.

Makes 20 balls. 2 balls are 10 g CHO. 100 kcals.

Marzipan Balls

This marzipan is not as smooth as the kind you make with icing sugar, but still manages to taste authentic.

50 g (2 oz) dried figs, chopped
50 ml (2 fl oz) water
½ tsp almond essence
colouring (optional)
50 g (2 oz) ground almonds

25 g (1 oz) porridge oats,
  ground fine
a little unsweetened
  desiccated coconut

Heat the dried figs and water in a pan until all the water is absorbed. Blend to a smooth paste then leave until cool.

Add the almond essence and colouring, if using. Work in the ground almonds and ground oats until a paste is formed. Chill in the fridge for 30 minutes before using.

Divide the chilled marzipan paste into 20 small balls. Roll the balls in the coconut. (If you have tiny shape cutters you could pat the paste out to just under 1 cm (⅜ inch) thickness and cut shapes out of it.)

Makes 20 balls. 4 balls are 10 g CHO. 100 kcals.

Stuffed Dates

This is a very attractive party sweet. The green-coloured marzipan stuffed into a date half looks very attractive and makes an eye-catching centrepiece. This dish originates from the Middle East.

1 quantity marzipan paste (see previous recipe)
green colouring

150 g (5 oz) fresh dates (equivalent to 9–12 dates)

When making the marzipan paste add green colouring to the paste. Cut the dates in half and take out the stones. Divide the chilled marzipan paste into as many pieces as you have date halves (18–24) and roll into oval shapes before pressing into the dates. Arrange the dates on a plate. If you are storing them in the fridge cover with foil.

Total CHO 145 g. 860 kcals.

Stuffed Dates with Apricot Cream

If you prefer your fillings creamy rather than nutty make up 1 quantity of apricot cream icing (p. 114). Spoon the cream into the 18-24 date halves. You can add a little yellow colouring to the apricot cream to make it a more vivid yellow and give a stronger effect against the dark colour of the dates.

Total CHO 110 g. 495 kcals.

Stuffed Prunes

An after-dinner treat for special meals. The soft, cooked prunes are filled with creamy apricot icing.

100 g (4 oz) stoned prunes (about 13 prunes with stones – see recipe)

½ quantity apricot cream icing (p. 114)

Pour just enough boiling water over the prunes to cover them and leave overnight. They will plump up in the water. In the morning take out the stones and put the water and prunes in a small pan and cook until soft. Pat dry on paper towels. Put a teaspoon of the icing in each of the prunes. Serve in little paper cases.

3 stuffed prunes are 10 g CHO. 50 kcals.

Strawberry Ice Cream

400 g (14 oz) strawberries   150 ml (5 fl oz) low-fat natural
2 tbls lemon juice   yogurt

Liquidize the strawberries together with the lemon juice until a thick even liquid is formed. Add yogurt and mix again. Pour into a foil tin or ice tray, cover with foil and leave in the freezer for about an hour until the sides begin to set. Then take out of freezer and whisk again in the liquidizer. Return to foil tin and freezer and leave to harden. Half an hour before serving put in the fridge so that it is easier to slice.

This quantity makes 8 portions and each portion is 5 g CHO. Note that it is necessary to thaw slightly this ice cream before cutting it. If you are only serving 1 portion at a time, the ice cream will not respond well to repeated thawings. One way to avoid this problem is to set the ice cream in smaller containers. Tin foil or small plastic containers are particularly useful. You could use 4 small containers, each one containing 2 servings. Cover when freezing.

Makes 8 servings. Each serving is 5 g CHO. 25 kcals.

SUGGESTIONS FOR SERVING

Ice cream served with cake always makes it that bit more special. Strawberry ice cream goes well with carob cake or pineapple fruit cake.

The ice cream can be served with 5g CHO of sultanas chopped in half. This makes it sweeter and rather different. Slices of fruit can also be used to garnish the ice cream. Strawberries would be the ideal choice.

Peach Yogurt Ice Cream

625 g (1 lb 6 oz) peaches (5   2 tbls lemon juice
   peaches)   150 ml (5 oz) low-fat yogurt

Peel the peaches and cut into chunks for the liquidizer. Blend with the lemon juice. Add yogurt and whisk again. Pour into tin foil container or ice tray, cover with foil and freeze for about an hour. The sides should just be beginning to set. Take out of the freezer and whisk again in the blender, beating air into the mixture. Pour back into container and leave to harden in the freezer. Put in the fridge to thaw slightly 30 minutes before serving.

This quantity makes 6 portions. See strawberry ice cream, previous page, on ways of avoiding repeatedly thawing and refreezing the ice cream. This is a sweet ice cream with a very smooth texture.

Makes 6 large servings. Each serving is 10 g CHO. 45 kcals.

Orange-Banana-Carrot Ice

A refreshing fruit and vegetable ice.

2 oranges, each weighing 150 g (5 oz), chopped
100 g (4 oz) banana, peeled, mashed

200 g (7 oz) carrot, finely grated
100 ml (4 fl oz) water

Combine all the ingredients in the blender to make a creamy mixture. Pour into ice trays. After freezing for an hour take out and blend again and then put back in the freezer to become firm. This can be served before it has become completely firm. If it is set, put in the fridge to thaw slightly before serving.

Makes 10 servings. Each serving is 5 g CHO. 20 kcals.

Carob Rum Raisin Ice Cream

This ice cream has a solid creamy texture even though it has a low fat content. It is strictly delicious.

90 g (3½ oz) raisins
225 g (8 oz) skimmed milk quark
150 ml (5 fl oz) low-fat natural yogurt

30 g (generous 1 oz) carob powder
1½–2 tsp rum or rum essence
2 egg whites, stiffly beaten

Leave the raisins to soak in a little water for a couple of hours before using. Boil them in their soaking water so that it is all absorbed. Grind them to a fine paste in a grinder, blender or food processor.

Combine the quark, yogurt and carob and mix well. Add the rum and ground raisins, again mixing well so that they are distributed throughout the mixture. Fold in the stiffly-beaten egg whites and turn into a foil container or mould. Cover and freeze. Half an hour before serving put in the fridge so that it is easier to slice. (See strawberry ice cream (p. 106) for suggestions on freezing different quantities.)

Makes 10 slices. Each slice is 10 g CHO. 55 kcals.

Tofu Carob Date Ice Cream

This recipe is milk free and egg free and ideal for anyone who needs to keep these ingredients out of their diets. My husband, on a working visit to New York, discovered that tofu ice cream, in a dozen different flavours, was all the rage in Manhattan, with vendors selling it on busy street corners. This recipe is made of carob and dates and is one they hadn't heard of in America.

90 g (3½ oz) dried dates
50 ml (2 fl oz) water
200 g (7 oz) firm tofu
150 ml (6 fl oz) soya milk

30 g (generous 1 oz) carob powder
1 tsp vanilla

Put the dates and water in a small pan over a low heat until the water is absorbed. Blend to make a smooth paste. Blend the tofu and soya milk to make a creamy liquid. Add the carob, vanilla and date paste. Pour into a foil container or mould. Cover with foil and leave in the freezer for about an hour until the sides begin to set. Then take out of the freezer and whisk in the liquidizer. This improves the final texture of the ice cream.

Half an hour before serving put the ice cream in the fridge so that it is easier to slice. (See strawberry ice cream (p. 106) for suggestions on freezing different quantities.)

Makes 8 slices. Each slice is 10 g CHO. 70 kcals.

Ice Lollies

200 ml (7 fl oz) unsweetened   200 ml (7 fl oz) water
   orange juice

Mix the orange juice and water well and pour into moulds. This amount makes 8 good-sized ice lollies.

Total CHO 20 g. 80 kcals.

Carob Banana Lollies

Bananas, when frozen, taste something like a rather thick vanilla ice cream. The following two recipes both use banana as a base, with sweet sauces frozen around them. They are popular with young and old.

2 bananas (each banana weighing   25 ml (1 fl oz) unsweetened
   100 g (4 oz) when peeled)   orange juice
25 g (1 oz) carob powder   25 ml (1 fl oz) water

Cut each banana into 5 pieces. Combine the carob with orange juice and water to make a paste. Dip the pieces of banana in the carob paste so that they become covered all over. The paste may become a little dry while you are dipping the banana, so moisten by adding a little more water. Freeze on a foil tray in the freezer. When the banana pieces are frozen they can all be stored in a freezer bag.

Makes 10 lollies. Each lolly is 5g CHO. 20 kcals.

Date Banana Lollies

Another delicious frozen banana recipe.

150 g (5 oz) peeled banana   50 g (2 oz) unsweetened
50 g (2 oz) dried dates   desiccated coconut
50 ml (2 fl oz) water

Cut the banana into 6 pieces, approximately 2.5–5 cm (1–2 inches) wide. Cook the date block in the water until it becomes a smooth paste. Blend if necessary. Leave until cool.

Coat the bananas in the date paste and then roll in the coconut. Freeze. If you are making a lot of these at one go, freeze them on a flat tray and then pack together in a foil box or freezer bag.

Makes 6 lollies. Each lolly is 10 g CHO. 90 kcals.

Sweet Barley

Ever since I was a child sitting in the steaming, warm kitchen in winter and watching my mother make barley soup, I have loved eating barley. Barley is a grain and can serve as an alternative to wheat. As with wheat you want to enjoy the high fibre benefits of this cereal; make sure that the outer husk has not been removed. Your local wholefood shop is probably the best source. If you are not used to this grain, this recipe for sweetened barley is a way of getting to know it. The quantities here are quite small and you might want to double them for large meals.

200 g (7 oz) cooked barley (about 50 g [2 oz] uncooked barley, see recipe)	1 tsp cinnamon
	50 ml (2 fl oz) rose water
	50 ml (2 fl oz) water
25 g (1 oz) dried figs, chopped	25 g (1 oz) flaked almonds
25 g (1 oz) sultanas	

The barley takes 30–45 minutes to cook in a pan covered with water. Simmer, with a lid on the pan, until the barley is soft and the cooking water absorbed.

Heat the figs, sultanas and cinnamon in a small pan with the rose water and water. Stir until the figs become mushy and the water turns into a thick paste. Stir in the cooked barley so that it becomes coated with the sweet perfumed paste. Take off the heat and stir in the flaked almonds. Serve either hot or cold.

Makes 6 servings. Each serving is 10 g CHO. 70 kcals.

Popcorn

This is an old favourite. Popcorn is tasty just by itself; it really does not need to be sprinkled with salt or icing sugar. These are fun for children to make.

oil
100g (4 oz) popcorn kernels
   (available from health food
   shops)

Use a heavy saucepan with a tight-fitting lid. Lightly cover the bottom of the saucepan with oil and heat. Add the popcorn kernels so that they just cover the bottom of the pan. Put on the saucepan lid. Very shortly the kernels will begin to pop – don't open the lid or they will be popping all over the kitchen. Shake the pan a little as they pop and when the noises have stopped take off the heat.

Makes enough for 4. A quarter of the total is 10 g CHO. 95 kcals.

Carob Milk Shake

A drink that is different but brimming with all the 'right' nutrients.

200 ml (7 fl oz) ($\frac{1}{3}$ pt) skimmed $\frac{1}{8}$ tsp cinnamon
   milk   a spot of vanilla
2 tsp carob powder

Put all the ingredients in the blender until frothy. Serve with ice cubes in the summer.

Milk shake is 10 g CHO. 75 kcals.

ICING AND DECORATION

Icing can transform a cake as if by magic. An ordinary cake becomes festive and exciting. Clearly this is not something you are going to do every time you bake a cake. But diabetic cakes do not always have to look austere, they too can be covered in sticky, melting and fragrant icings!

There are a great range of materials you can use, not only in the icings but also as decoration.

Fresh fruit, particularly fruit like cherries or strawberries, blackberries or apricots, is colourful and can be cut into thin slices to gain maximum effect.

Dried fruit can also be used effectively, but has a high carbohydrate content so has to be used sparingly as there is no point in having decorations which add greatly to the carbohydrate value.

Flowers can be used to decorate quickly cakes and create a very dramatic and colourful effect.

Colouring: it is normally easy to obtain the basic colours of red, blue and green. These can be mixed or used in different strengths to obtain a variety of colours.

Some people are allergic to artificial colours and need to use colours from natural sources. Some alternative colours sources are:

yellow – saffron, carrot juice
red – beetroot juice, blackcurrant juice (squeezed from the fruit)
light brown – cinnamon

Carob Fudge Icing

This is just delicious. This recipe makes a very thick fudgy icing. It does add carbohydrates on to the cake's total so if you want to add fruit decorations as well, use a fruit that is hardly counted such as half a dozen cherries or strawberries. Remember to use fruit with a colour that will show up against the carob background.

25 g (1 oz) carob powder	10 g (⅓ oz) porridge oats,
25 g (1 oz) margarine	finely ground
50 ml (2 fl oz) skimmed milk	1 tsp rum essence or rum

Put the carob, margarine and milk in a small pan over a low heat to enable the margarine to melt. Add the ground oats and take off the heat. Add the rum. You can spread this icing on the cake while it is still warm. This quantity covers an 18 cm (7 inch) cake quite thickly.

Icing is 20 g CHO. 290 kcals.

Quick Carob Icing

This recipe requires no cooking and can be thrown together in a matter of minutes. When the icing is fresh on the cake it glistens.

25 g (1 oz) tahini	50 ml (2 fl oz) unsweetened
10 g (⅓ oz) carob powder	orange juice

Mix the tahini and carob and add enough orange juice to make a more liquid paste suitable for spreading on a cake. Sufficient to cover a 20–23 cm (8–9 inch) diameter cake.

Icing is 15 g CHO. 185 kcals.

Carob Cream Icing

15 g (½ oz) dates	½ tsp vanilla
100 g (4 oz) skimmed milk quark	½ tsp cinnamon
15 g (½ oz) carob powder	

Put the dates in a pan with a little water and cook over a low heat to make a thick paste. Work in a blender until smooth. Mix the date paste with the quark, carob, cinnamon and vanilla. Stir well so that all ingredients are worked evenly into the cheese. Enough to cover a 20 cm (8 inch) diameter cake.

Icing is 20 g CHO. 145 kcals.

Apricot Cream Icing

This is a sweet-tasting, pale yellow cream.

25 g (1 oz) dried apricots 1 dessertspoon lemon juice
100 g (4 oz) skimmed milk quark

For this recipe it is necessary to chop the apricots very finely. I use the coffee-grinding attachment to the blender. Alternatively you can chop by hand or use a food processor. Chop or grind the apricots until they are reduced to small dots. Mix with the quark and lemon juice. It is ready for spreading straight away. Enough to cover a 20 cm (8 inch) diameter cake.

Icing is 15 g CHO. 125 kcals.

Coconut Cream Icing

This has a subtle coconut taste. It gives a thin coating over a cake. Because it is white you can add to it whatever colour you want. It also has negligible carbohydrate content but should be eaten in small quantities because coconut has a high saturated fat content.

25 g (1 oz) coconut cream colouring (optional)
75 ml (3 fl oz) water

Gently heat the coconut cream and water in a small pan until the coconut cream is broken down and absorbed by the water to make a thickish paste suitable for spreading. Use plain or add colouring.

Icing is 0 g CHO. 160 kcals.

SUGGESTIONS FOR USE

Cupcakes: add green colouring to the icing. Spread over the top of cupcakes and decorate with a sliver of banana on top.
– Colour alone is very effective. Mix up two bowls of pink and green icing. Put a teaspoon of each colour on the cupcake so that the top is half green and half pink. This is quick to do and the result is bright and festive.
– For a children's party mix up pink icing and make faces (green for Martians): two eyes out of little bits of banana, a mouth out of cherry or red apple peel and a blob of grape for the nose.

– Snowmen: use very deep patty tins so that when the cake is turned upside down it is deeper than it is wide. Cover with white coconut cream icing and chopped up raisins for eyes and mouth. A thin strip of dried apricot cut all the way round makes a small scarf for the snowman. If the tin you use does not give a long enough body shape, stick a head on top of the snowman. A large grape covered in coconut cream icing would give the right proportions.

Coloured Coconut

Unsweetened desiccated coconut mixed with a colour and sprinkled over a cake thinly covered in jam, gives a grassy or furry effect. Owing to its high saturated fat content (although it has almost no carbohydrate content) this type of decoration is recommended mainly for birthdays and very special occasions.

GRASS DESIGNS

Mix the coconut with a few drops of green colouring for a rich grass colour. Lightly cover the surface of the cake with sugar-free jam (25 g sugar-free jam is 10 g CHO) and sprinkle the coconut on top. This makes an effective lawn. Use it with the following ideas:

Park cake: put a toy slide in the middle of the grass and a couple of little toy children on or around the slide.

Football pitch cake: use a couple of white pipe cleaners to make goal posts, mark up the pitch with piped apricot cream icing and put on a few toy footballers.

Flower garden cake: decorate with some of the flowers that appear in the flower section (p. 121).

OTHER IDEAS WITH COLOURED COCONUT

CATERPILLAR CAKE: This is great fun for children. If your maths is good you can even make it so that each segment of the caterpillar's body is 10 g CHO. Make 12 cakes in deep jam tart tins or patty tins. Turn them upside down and lightly cover with jam and green coconut. Use a large plate or silver-paper covered base on which to put the segments into a long curvey line. Use a couple of raisins for eyes for the head. For the caterpillar's little legs, which go all down the length of its body, use thin strips of dried apricot, or cut-up multi-coloured straws, spearing a raisin at the bottom for little feet!

Caterpillar cake

TEDDY BEAR OR PUSSY CAT CAKES: There are two ways to go about these. The easy method is to draw a large but simple teddy bear or cat on the surface of the cake and just fill this shape with either yellow or brown coconut for the teddy bear and brown coconut with a few yellow stripes for the cat. The rest of the cake can be decorated with carob cream icing as background. Use currants for eyes, little bits of red apple peel for nostrils and mouth. Straws are good for whiskers and if these go over the edge of the cake it only adds to the effect.

The more difficult method is after having drawn your shape on the cake to cut around it. The advantage is that you have a complete animal shape. The disadvantage is that cake is left over which you need to include in the teddy bear or cat shape for the sake of the carbohydrate and calorie count. The simplest method is to cut it into thin slices and evenly place it under the animal shape. It will still be quite hard to work out how to cut a cat or teddy bear into 10 grams of carbohydrate! – a round or square shape is obviously easier to cut into equal amounts. Decorate the cut-out animal completely with desiccated coconut and put in eyes, nose, etc. If the shape is large enough half a strawberry can make a very good nose.

MORE DECORATION IDEAS

When decorating cakes remember to add on the carbohydrate value of the icing you use and the dried or fresh fruit. Usually one does not want to have to add on a lot more carbohydrates or calories, so decorating becomes an exercise in using icings and decorations sparingly but to good effect.

HAPPY BIRTHDAY CAKES: cover the cake in one of the carob icings or the apricot cream icing. If the background is carob cream icing use the apricot cream icing to pipe 'Happy Birthday' on to the cake. Alternatively, 'Happy Birthday' can be written in thin slices of dried fruit, fresh fruit or marzipan (p. 104). Roll the marzipan into long thin strips like plasticine and make it into letters.

CLOCK CAKE: use a round cake as the base. Use one of the carob icings or the apricot cream icing for the face and a different colour icing (or desiccated coconut) for the sides. This sets off the face more strongly. You need to put numbers and hands on this cake. Straws make the straightest hands and can be cut to size. Numbers can be piped on using the carob cream icing or apricot cream icing, or orange peel can be cut up to make numbers, or slivers of dried fruit such as apricots and raisins. If the clock face is carob you will need to use bright colours to show up on it; dried fruit, which is better on a paler background, will not be strong enough. Put a cherry, strawberry or grape where the two hands of the clock meet in the middle of the cake.

60 CAKE: use a round cake as a base because the outside of the '6' and '0' are both round and you should be able to draw these figures so that they follow part of the outline of the cake. Fill in the numbers with a different coloured icing from the surrounding area so that the contrast highlights them. Pipe a thin outline around the numbers using carob cream icing or apricot cream icing, or use thin slivers of dried or fresh fruit for the outline.

VALENTINE CAKE: use a heart-shaped tin and your favourite cake recipe. Cover with one of the icings in this section and pipe with carob cream icing or apricot cream icing or use fresh or dried fruit slivers for the message 'Be My Valentine' or 'I Love You'.

An unusual Valentine cake is one made of ice cream. Use three or four times the quantity of one of the ice cream recipes in this book and pour into a heart-shaped tin that can be put in a freezer. Strawberry ice cream or carob ice cream both make a lovely rich coloured base, so all you need to do is pipe on your message with carob cream icing or apricot cream icing and a few stars around the sides and, if you can find one, lay a wild violet flower on top. You might find that the ice cream comes out of the tin best when it has been in the fridge for half an hour. You will then need to act fast. Turn the ice cream upside down, decorate and serve. A calmer alternative is to serve the cake in the tin. This leaves time to decorate the ice cream when set and return to the freezer until it is needed. When serving cover the tin with silver foil or a pretty ribbon so that it becomes part of the final effect.

CASTLE CAKE (with a wicked witch or a lovely princess): use 2 cakes: a 20 cm (8 inch) square, 7.5 cm (3 inches) deep as a base for the castle, and a 10 × 20 cm × 2.5 cm (4 × 8 × 1 inch) shallow cake for the battlements. Cut the shallow cake in half lengthways.

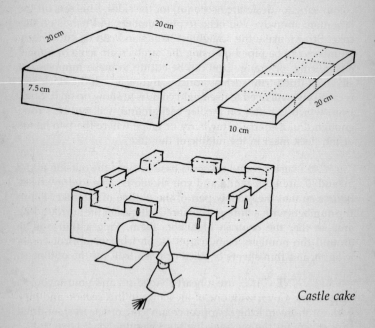

Castle cake

Divide each half into 4 pieces and fix them a little apart from each other with a toothpick on to the base of the cake.

Cover the cake with a double quantity of carob cream icing or apricot cream icing. Decorate with slivers of apricot for windows. Make a door to the castle using a contrasting icing. The battlements can be highlighted by outlining them with slivers of fruit or strips of light green apple peel. The witch or princess (use a small plastic figure, if it does not quite fit the part, dress in a foil cloak and hat and cover this with icing) can either stand behind the battlements or in front of the castle door.

SCONE DOUGH FOR NUMBERS AND SHAPES

The plain scone dough (p. 83) is an ideal base for numbers and shapes. This is a soft malleable dough rolled out to just under 1 cm (⅜ inch) thickness. A double quantity of the recipe would be sufficient to make 2 large numbers '70' or '50'. You don't even need to roll out the dough. Divide it in half and work it with your hands into the number you need. If you are making 2 numbers be sure that they are both the same height and roughly the same width so they look as if they belong to each other.

This dough can also be used to make shapes of animals. If you aren't too confident about doing these shapes, you could take a large magazine picture and fit the dough to the picture or figures. The scone shapes can be left plain or decorated as with the other cakes in this section. An effective method is to cover the surface with jam and sprinkle with apple flakes (10 grams of apple flakes are 10 grams carbohydrate).

Draught set or chess set: use two thirds of the dough to make the board. Use the quick carob icing for the dark squares. Make the remaining dough into the draughts. You could either mix a little carob into half of this dough for the dark draughts or cover with quick carob icing.

Making chess pieces is strictly for those with lots of time and dedication.

SAVOURY DECORATIONS

Skimmed milk quark, without a sweetener, can be used as a decoration for savoury dishes. For variety add colouring to the quark.

DOMINOES: use carob scone dough (p. 84). Roll out and cut into identical oblongs about 7.5 × 2.5 cm (3 × 1 inches). Pipe on plain quark for the dots and lines.

MAP: if someone is off to Australia or America for a while, make a scone map of where they are going. Trace a large map on greaseproof paper, place on the rolled-out dough and cut around. When baked cover with quark. Chopped parsley makes trees, sliced dark-green olives for swamps, thinly sliced red peppers make a vivid coastal outline, flower petals for lakes, cooked aduki beans for mountain ranges. If you prefer to colour the quark, tint

Cottage

it yellow for desert, brown – and lifted into little peaks with a fork – for mountain ranges, and green for vast plains.

COTTAGE: take a small wholewheat loaf of bread for your base. If the top is curvey even better, as it will make a good roof. Cut the loaf lengthways three or four times and fill each slice with colourful sandwich fillings (e.g. tuna, mashed avocado, cooked yellow corn mixed with red peppers). Cover the whole loaf with plain quark and decorate with vegetables: round tomato windows, thin strips of carrot for a thatched roof, cucumber cut lengthways for a door and radish cut into flower shapes to put by the door.

FLOWERS

Flowers have a part to play in decorating sugar-free cakes. They are quick to use and add a blaze of colour to your cakes, lifting them from the mundane to the extraordinary. They were used in cooking in England in the days of Shakespeare and Queen Elizabeth I. They are still used today in Middle Eastern and Japanese cooking. The flowers named here are edible but they can just be used for their decorative effect and removed before eating.

HOW TO USE FLOWERS
– Do not use flowers that have been sprayed with chemicals while they were growing. The best flowers to use are those you have grown yourself. A green-fingered gardener of my acquaintance recommends using a soapy liquid to spray over greenfly.
– Always wash and drain flowers before use.
– Either put the flowers directly on the cake or else use a white coconut cream icing as background. This icing is good because it sets hard and does not stick to the flowers.

Carnation – dianthus carnation: these are small carnation flowers that do not grow in a hothouse. They are usually red, pink or striped. Wash and drain the flowers and cut off at the base of the flower. Place around the cake to decorate.

Marigolds – calendula officinalis: the golden-yellow petals of this flower will add a blaze of colour to any dish. Remove the petals from fresh marigolds and wash and drain them. You can make attractive patterns on a cake with these petals. Use on a coconut cream icing background.

Roses: the best roses to use are the old fashioned varieties or the wild rose. Modern hybrid roses have tougher petals which makes them suitable for decoration only. Wash and dry rose petals. Sprinkle them liberally over cakes or over little cupcakes.

Violets – viola odorata: this is the wild purple violet found growing in the spring. Remove the blossoms from the stems and wash and drain. The small petal flower is used for decoration. Very attractive to garnish a dish of ice cream.

FOOD VALUES

(neg = negligible;
n/a = information not available)

Food	Amount	CHO approx	Calories approx	Fibre approx
Almonds, shelled	25 g (1 oz)	neg	140	3.6 g
Apple, eating, medium	110 g (4 oz)	10 g	40	1.7 g
Apple flakes	25 g (1 oz)	23 g	90	n/a
Apple juice, unsweetened	150 ml (5 fl oz)	18 g	70	neg
Apricots, dried raw	25 g (1 oz)	10 g	45	6.0 g
Apricots, fresh	160 g (5½ oz)	10 g	40	3.0 g
Banana, peeled	50 g (2 oz)	10 g	40	1.7 g
Barley, raw	25 g (1 oz)	18 g	85	0.9 g
Barley flour	25 g (1 oz)	19 g	90	0.6 g
Beans, aduki, raw	25 g (1 oz)	10 g	70	6.3 g
Blackberries, raw	160 g (5½ oz)	10 g	45	11.7 g
Bran, wheat	25 g (1 oz)	5 g	45	11.0 g
Carob powder	25 g (1 oz)	12 g	50	13.8 g
Carrot, raw	100 g (4 oz)	11 g	45	5.8 g
Carrot juice	25 ml (1 fl oz)	n/a	n/a	neg
Cherries, fresh whole	100 g (4 oz)	10 g	40	1.5 g
Chestnuts, dried	25 g (1 oz)	22 g	105	n/a
Chestnuts, fresh, skinned	25 g (1 oz)	10 g	45	1.7 g
Coconut cream	25 g (1 oz)	neg	160	n/a
Coconut, desiccated	25 g (1 oz)	neg	150	5.9 g
Corn (maize) meal	15 g (½ oz)	11 g	55	0.3 g
Cottage cheese	25 g (1 oz)	neg	25	neg
Dates, dried without stones	15 g (½ oz)	10 g	30	1.1 g
Dates, fresh	50 g (2 oz)	10 g	40	n/a
Egg, size 3	1	neg	75	neg
Figs, dried raw	20 g ⅔ oz)	10 g	40	3.7 g
Flour, brown rice	25 g (1 oz)	20 g	90	n/a
Flour, soya, low fat	35 g (1⅓ oz)	10 g	125	5.0 g
Flour, wholewheat	15 g (½ oz)	10 g	50	1.4 g
Jam, sugar-free	25 g (1 oz)	9 g	30	n/a

Food	Amount	CHO approx	Calories approx	Fibre approx
Kombu	25 g (1 oz)	n/a	n/a	n/a
Margarine, polyunsaturated	25 g (1 oz)	neg	185	neg
Marmalade, sugar-free	25 g (1 oz)	9 g	30	n/a
Milk, skimmed	200 ml (7 fl oz)	10 g	65	neg
Millet flakes	15 g (½ oz)	11 g	55	0.7 g
Oats, porridge	15 g (½ oz)	11 g	60	1.1 g
Oat bran (with germ)	25 g (1 oz)	15 g	105	3.5 g
Oil (sunflower, soya bean, vegetable)	15 ml (½ fl oz)	neg	135	neg
Orange, whole	150 g (5 oz)	10 g	40	2.3 g
Orange juice	100 ml (4 fl oz)	10 g	40	neg
Papaya (flesh only)	80 g (3 oz)	10 g	40	0.4 g
Peach, fresh whole	125 g (4½ oz)	10 g	40	1.5 g
Peanut butter, natural	25 g (1 oz)	5 g	160	1.9 g
Pineapple, fresh (flesh only)	90 g (3½ oz)	10 g	40	1.1 g
Plums, dessert	110 g (4 oz)	10 g	40	2.2 g
Poppy seeds	25 g (1 oz)	5 g	140	n/a
Potato, mashed (no milk, butter)	50 g (2 oz)	10 g	40	0.5 g
Prunes, dried, no stones	25 g (1 oz)	10 g	35	3.4 g
Pumpkin, cooked	100 g (4 oz)	1 g	10	0.6 g
Pumpkin seeds	25 g (1 oz)	5 g	140	1.0 g
Quark, skimmed milk	50 g (2 oz)	3 g	40	neg
Raisins	15 g (½ oz)	10 g	35	1.0 g
Rice, brown	25 g (1 oz)	20 g	90	0.2 g
Rice flakes, brown	25 g (1 oz)	20 g	90	0.2 g
Rose water	25 ml (1 fl oz)	neg	neg	neg
Rye flour	25 g (1 oz)	19 g	85	n/a
Sesame seeds	25 g (1 oz)	5 g	145	1.3 g
Shredded wheat	1 bar	18 g	80	3.3 g
Soya milk	200 ml (7 fl oz)	7 g	210	neg
Strawberries, fresh	160 g (5½ oz)	10 g	40	3.5 g
Sultanas	15 g (½ oz)	10 g	40	1.0 g
Sunflower seeds	25 g (1 oz)	5 g	140	0.9 g
Tahini (sesame seed paste)	25 g (1 oz)	5 g	145	1.3 g
Tofu (soya bean curd)	100 g (4 oz)	3 g	55	neg
Walnuts, shelled	25 g (1 oz)	neg	130	1.3 g
Wheat germ	25 g (1 oz)	11 g	85	n/a
Yogurt, natural, low-fat	150 ml (5 fl oz)	10 g	80	neg

SELECT BIBLIOGRAPHY

Budd, Martin, *Diets to Help Diabetics*, Thorsons, 1984.

Cleave, T. L., *The Saccharine Disease*, J. Wright, 1974.

Coultate, T. P., *Food: the Chemistry of its Components*, Royal Society of Chemistry, 1984.

Dark, R., *Dried Fruit*, Thorsons, 1982.

Hanley, Zack., *Cooking with Flowers*, New English Library, 1971.

McCance and Widdowson, *The Composition of Foods*, HMSO, 1979.

Mount, James Lambert, *The Food and Health of Western Man*, Charles Knight, 1975.

Sams, C., *About Macrobiotics*, Thorsons, 1984.

Spry, Constance, *Come into the Garden, Cook*, J. M. Dent, 1942.

Stanway, Andrew, *Taking the Rough with the Smooth*, Souvenir Press, 1976.

INDEX